THE PATTEN FOUNDATION

Mr. Will Patten of Indianapolis (A.B., Indiana University, 1893) made, in 1931, a gift for the establishment of the Patten Foundation at his Alma Mater. Under the terms of this gift, which became available upon the death of Mr. Patten (May 3, 1936), there is to be chosen each year a Visiting Professor who is to be in residence several weeks during the year. The purpose of this prescription is to provide an opportunity for members and friends of the University to enjoy the privilege and advantage of personal acquaintance with the Visiting Professor. The Visiting Professor for the Patten Foundation in 1949–50 was

PROFESSOR L. DUDLEY STAMP

"Fourth, we must embark on a bold new program for making the benefits of our scientific advances and industrial progress available for the improvement and growth of under-developed areas. More than half the people of the world are living in conditions approaching misery. Their food is inadequate. They are victims of disease. Their economic life is primitive and stagnant. Their poverty is a handicap and a threat both to them and to more prosperous areas. For the first time in history, humanity possesses the knowledge and the skill to relieve the suffering of these people."

President Truman in his Inaugural Address, January 20, 1949

"Be it enacted by the King's most Excellent Majesty, by and with the advice and consent of the Lords Spiritual and Temporal, and Commons, in this present Parliament assembled, and by the authority of the same, as follows:—The Secretary of State, with the concurrence of the Treasury, may make schemes for any purpose likely to promote the development of the resources of any colony or the welfare of its people, and any sums required by the Secretary of State for the purpose of any such scheme shall be paid out of moneys provided by Parliament."

Colonial Development and Welfare Act, 1940. July 17, 1940

Land
for Tomorrow

THE UNDERDEVELOPED WORLD

BY L. Dudley Stamp

BLOOMINGTON:
Indiana University Press

NEW YORK:
American Geographical Society

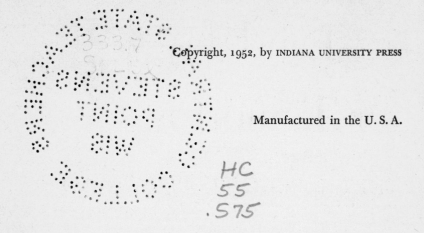

CONTENTS

Preface

No PROBLEM confronting us today is more important than that of matching the world's use of its natural resources with the needs of its people. Since food is essential to all life, the use of land for food production is always in the forefront of the picture. In recent years the urgency of the problems of food supply has been brought home to some countries by acute shortages, a restricted dietary, or rationing, to others by soaring prices. International gatherings, official and unofficial, have debated the many complex issues involved; the United Nations has set up the World Food and Agriculture Organization (FAO); many books have appeared ranging from the almost hysterically pessimistic to the ebulliently optimistic. Even when discussion is on a world basis, views are too frequently colored by national backgrounds. Nevertheless, rising above all of them are such declarations as President Truman's Point IV and the preamble from the British Colonial Development and Welfare Act which indicate clearly the sense of responsibility shared by the English-speaking world. Independent of domestic problems, though inseparable from these, is the realization that help must be afforded to the underdeveloped lands of the world that they may play their part both in working out their own salvation and in helping to ameliorate the general world situation.

This book is based on the Patten Foundation Lectures which I delivered at Indiana University in 1950. In it I have tried to collect in small compass what seem to me to be significant facts and figures from which the reader can form his own judgments. For the opportunity I am deeply grateful to the University, and especially to the Patten Foundation Committee, headed by its then chairman, Dr. Ralph E. Cleland, and to the members of the Department of Geography, headed by Dr. Otis P. Starkey. Six weeks' residence in the congenial and stimulating academic atmosphere of the charming campus at Bloomington gave me the welcome leisure to see in retrospect my own work in the field of land use over the last twenty years. Further, the University in accepting the responsibility for the publication of these lectures has given me a chance to acknowledge how much I owe to many good friends who have been my mentors or co-workers over that period.

In my early years of work in Burma and India, both in the field and in the University of Rangoon, I accepted as natural that little was published concerning the use of the land and the reasons for use or non-use, though I quickly learned to respect the fund of rural knowledge possessed by almost every village cultivator. On returning to academic life in England, I realized with some surprise how much remained to be learned in even that long-settled and well-documented land. When I established the Land Utilisation Survey of Britain in 1930, it was with the object of recording the then-existing use of every acre in England, Wales, and Scotland, and of attempting to discover the reasons for that use. The field work of my many thousand volunteers was virtually complete, but the interpretation of the results had only just begun, when the late Dr. Isaiah Bowman, to whom I am everlastingly grateful, suggested and afterwards made it possible for me to spend the academic year 1933-34 in America. So it came about that, with my wife as co-chauffeur, I saw the United States in and out of Prohibition, in depression and drought, under N.R.A. with the New Deal newly dealt and the T.V.A. undergoing severe teething troubles. I visited eastern Canada in the full glory of the fall, and my travels took me to every one of the forty-eight states of the Union. Three months were occupied by an attempt to see something of land-use problems in each of the South American republics, excepting only Paraguay. On my return to Britain I found that the methods of the Land Utilisation Survey—the careful factual survey and the subsequent objective interpretation—had attracted attention elsewhere. Though the proposal that I should inaugurate a similar survey for China was frustrated by the Japanese invasions, I did reach the border of China and spend some time in Siam and my old haunts in Burma and Malaya. Field work in West Africa had already convinced me that there was much to learn from native agricultural practices throughout the tropics, while conferences throughout India showed how badly needed was a Land Use Survey there.

What had been an academic exercise took on an unexpected significance when World War II broke out in September, 1939. Both the field maps and published one-inch maps of the Land Utilisation Survey were in demand in connection with the intensive drive to increase home food production. Even in the darkest days Britain had half an eye on postwar problems, and my appointment as Adviser to the newly formed British Ministry of Works and Buildings began a long association as adviser to various government departments, though I successfully escaped becoming a civil servant. Outstanding events that I recall with gratitude were the long week ends I spent as Vice-Chairman of Lord Justice Scott's Committee on Land Utilisation in Rural Areas. I drafted the report at the country home of one who was not only an outstanding Lord Justice of Appeal but also a charming host who taught me to realize, in its survival in him, the graciousness of the Victorian age.

National and local land use and agricultural planning derived in Britain from national necessity, not from political idealism. Both the Ministry of Town and Country Planning and the former Central Planning Branch of the Ministry of Agriculture were established by the wartime Coalition Government, each under a Conservative minister. To a very considerable extent physical planning has been kept out of politics. There was at all times a perfect freedom to develop objectively the study of land and its use. As Chief Adviser in Rural Land Use to the Minister of Agriculture, I had my team of ten Rural Land Utilisation Officers, each a man of standing in his own region, and together we thrashed out the principles to be adopted.

In Britain I have grown accustomed to the overriding consideration common to most of the Old World—that the prime shortage is a shortage of land. This is not yet the first, the most urgent, nor the most insistent aspect of the problem in America. Long discussions with the Canadian government at Ottawa in 1947 and conferences in the States from New York to California, as well as practical results from the acquisition of a Canadian island home in British Columbia, have shown me how very different are the problems here. This contrast was emphasized at the United Nations Scientific Conference on Conservation and Utilization of Resources held at Lake Success in August and September, 1949, when, as one of the representatives of Britain, I found myself expressing views very different from those of Mr. J. A. Krug, then Secretary of the Interior.

In the pages which follow I have attempted to deal frankly not only with the problems which my experience has taught me to expect but also with the differences which are clearly apparent between the viewpoints of the Old and New Worlds. What constitutes "underdevelopment" is in itself an interesting problem and is closely linked with two contrasted views of agricultural efficiency—output per unit area and output per manhour.

There now exists what may be called an "official" definition of underdeveloped lands. It is that used to determine whether a country is eligible for United States' assistance under the Point IV program and is based upon income per capita. If the income per head of population falls below a certain figure, the country is classed as underdeveloped. Although the result may be satisfactory from the point of view of the aid program, it would seem that it is poverty, not underdevelopment, which is being measured. To take a hypothetical case, there might not be a single farmer in the United States but, provided the income of the people remained above the datum line, the country could not be classed as "underdeveloped." On the other hand, by this definition India and China, even in their most crowded and intensively cultivated parts, are underdeveloped.

It is not the purpose of this book to present ready-made solutions to the many world problems it exposes; I am concerned rather that essential facts should be more widely known and understood.

In our new-found enthusiasm to help the peoples of the "underdeveloped lands" we may do irreparable harm if we take to alien environments preconceived knowledge or ready-made solutions based upon experience gained under other conditions. This is particularly the case when we attempt to take both our concepts of a "standard of living" and our agricultural techniques from mid-latitudes into tropical lands, about which we still know so little. Do we, for example, really know what and where "underdeveloped lands" are?

This is one of the questions I have asked myself and tried to answer in the following pages.

L.D.S.

Bloomington, Indiana, May 9, 1950

Since the Patten Lectures were delivered in March, April, and May, 1950, the world has not stood still and I have made certain corrections and additions. For many editorial suggestions I am greatly indebted to Dr. Gladys Wrigley, as all those who have contributed in past years to the *Geographical Review* will appreciate.

L.D.S.

November, 1951

CHAPTER I

The Problem

Backward areas" we used to call them—those countries which, by our western standards, lagged behind in the march of progress. But ours are not the only standards and, not unnaturally, many peoples living in the "backward areas" felt that the term conveyed both an unjust judgment and a reproach. If their countries were indeed backward, might it not be that they labored under handicaps not imposed on the more fortunate, might it not be that they were victims of historical and economic circumstances beyond their control, or even of past and present suppression or repression? Might it not also be that areas classed as backward in material progress were sometimes the homes of ethical, moral, and religious codes which had much to teach the Western world? So, with official endorsement by the United Nations, the word "backward" has been dropped and the word "underdeveloped" substituted. "Backward" involves subjective judgment; "underdeveloped" is merely an objective statement.

It is clear that when we of the Western world refer to the underdeveloped lands we are thinking essentially of areas, mainly within the tropics, where the inhabitants do not yet enjoy those material advantages which we associate with the phrase "a high standard of living." Some are lands where the natural forest or savanna hides but a handful of inhabitants and where none could dispute the term underdeveloped. Others are lands where man's conquest of the natural environment is far from complete, as in vast areas where cattle-keeping tribes on soil-eroded grasslands or primitive farmers scratching the land with a hoe and waiting for a precarious rainfall live constantly in fear of starvation. But shall we class as underdeveloped those lands where close-packed millions wrest a living from the soil, however inefficiently from our Western standpoint? We are, accordingly, led to inquire as to what is really meant by underdeveloped.

The famous Point IV proclaimed by President Truman supplies one definition. The underdeveloped areas are those areas where more than half the people of the world are living in conditions approaching misery, where food is inadequate, disease rampant, where economic life is primitive and stagnant, and where poverty is a lasting and dangerous handicap. This is clearly intended to cover both sparsely and densely populated areas and not merely those where natural resources remain unused.

Taking the words literally, there is the obvious interpretation of underdeveloped—that natural resources have not been developed to the full extent possible. The greatest of all natural resources is land, and there are parts of the world, in the Yangtze Delta for example, where the produce of a single square mile is sufficient to support several thousand human beings. There are some parts of India where a rural density of 1,000 a square mile prevails. Can we possibly class such lands as underdeveloped though the people may live in conditions approaching misery, handicapped in every direction by poverty?

Well-farmed European lands support one person or more an acre, 640 or more to the square mile, yet lands we think of as "developed" by our modern Western methods, in the United States, Canada, and Argentina, produce only enough food on a square mile to support some 200 or 240 persons. On the basis of output per acre we find the familiar mid-latitude or temperate lands of North America among the most underdeveloped lands in the world. If the object of "development" is to achieve maximum production or to support a maximum population, we have a long way to go before we can regard our own lands as fully developed. Yet the techniques of which we boast have been worked out to meet conditions as we know them best.

This brings us to the other aspect of the Point IV declaration: "For the first time in history humanity possesses the knowledge and the skill to relieve the suffering of these people [of the underdeveloped lands]." This is a bold statement, a proud boast; is it justified? The white man's medicine may indeed be able to conquer and cure many of the ills to which human flesh is prone, but not before diseases associated with Western civilization have taken such a toll of human lives as never before was imagined. We may even doubt whether our endeavor to keep alive the sickly, the incurably diseased, and the hopelessly deformed is really in keeping with the great design of Nature. The white man's weapons of war, on an ever-increasing scale of horror, are more destructive of the cream of human beings than ever before. Even when we turn to peaceful spheres, the greatest scourge known to man—that which truly threatens the slow extinction of the species—the scourge of soil erosion, is essentially a product of Western civilization. In a brief century our large-scale agriculture has destroyed the accumulated soil wealth of ages; and wherever we attempt "development" of new lands the same irretrievable loss is still liable to occur. Experience, in fact, constantly reveals our ignorance and confirms the need for humbly seeking new knowledge. Moreover, though the problem of the underdeveloped lands is immediate, it is also continuing and calls for continuous study.

Again and again we see the wisdom, even the vital necessity, of Man's entering into alliance with Nature instead of regarding himself as freed by his inventions from natural laws. Any geologist knows that erosion is a natural, inevitable, and continuing process that has been taking place since the world began. Watching the muddied waters of the Yellow River in northern China, the geologist visualizes the dustlike yellow loess from the arid heart of Asia being swept seawards where it will help slowly to build up those fertile delta lands capable of supporting vast numbers of people. This is a natural process, in the long run benefiting mankind. On the other hand, the watcher by the swollen muddied waters of the Mississippi in flood recognizes the mud as the soil of once fertile farmlands; the excess of water due to the destruction of forest and prairie; and the swift current as taking the solid burden far out to sea where it can have no value to man. Here a natural process has been so accelerated by man's interference that it is destructive in the extreme.

Thus, on the one hand we have the pessimists who see the destructive forces of nature unleashed and no hope for mankind but immediate and voluntary limitation of numbers. This, they say, is the only "road to survival." Others have full faith in the power of our modern knowledge to tame the wild. They see "new worlds emerging" in the dense forests of Brazil or the wide open savannas of Africa. If their visions are correct, and if the new worlds were developed so as to be as productive as the average well-farmed lands of, say, northwestern Europe, the world could well support four times its present population, or 10,000,000,000 people. Even so, population increase at present rates is such that the world's total can reach such figures within comparatively few generations. We are, however, concerned more with where we stand today.

CHAPTER II

The World's Peoples

No ONE KNOWS the exact population of the world, but it is certainly well over 2,000 million and is growing with ever-increasing rapidity. With the passage of years, census returns of greater or less accuracy are becoming available for an ever larger proportion of the earth's surface. In the 1930's, especially for the years 1930-31 during which so many national censuses were taken, it became possible to make a reasonable estimate of the world's population, with the margin of error being not more than a few per cent. The largest single source of error was, and still is, the population of China, for which no detailed census figures exist. For large parts of Africa also the figures are only rough estimates, though a previous major source of error was removed by the 1948 census in British East Africa. Sir Alexander Carr-Saunders in his book *World Population*, 1936, gives the sources of information then available with an assessment of their reliability and quotes the following totals for 1930: International Institute of Statistics, 1,988,279,000; International Yearbook of Agriculture Statistics, 2,012,810,000; Statistical Year Book

of the League of Nations, 2,028,200,000. The difference
in these estimates is only two per cent of the average,
but all three used the same imperfect sources in many
cases, for example, for most of Africa. At that same
time the late Dr. R. R. Kuczynski did not consider it
possible to do more than to say the population of the
world was between 1,880 and 2,260 millions, the possible error being ten per cent. Ten years later the
Statistical Year Book of the League of Nations gave the
total for 1940 as 2,145,000,000. The Demographic Yearbook of the Statistical Office of the United Nations for
1948 estimated the world population in mid-1947 at
2,325,834,000. The Food and Agriculture Organization
of the United Nations in its 1948 Yearbook of Food
and Agricultural Statistics gave estimates of 2,142,633,-
000 at mid-1937 and 2,314,553,000 at mid-1947. The
figures are stated to be based on "official estimates"
wherever feasible, sometimes with interpolated values,
and elsewhere on data supplied by the Statistical Office
of the United Nations. In the 1949 Yearbook, FAO
published the following revised estimates; 2,150,687,000
at mid-1937 and 2,354,128,000 at mid-1948.

The Department of Social Affairs of the United Nations has published its own summary entitled *World
Population Trends 1920-1947*. With due cautionary
notes, it summarizes the situation thus:

| 1920 | 1,778,000,000 | mid-1937 | 2,147,000,000 |
| 1930 | 1,988,000,000 | mid-1947 | 2,330,000,000 |

These data suggest that we are justified in using a

total of 2,350 million for the world family of 1950.
If we are dealing with the 1940-41 period—shortly after
the outbreak of World War II—a total of 2,200 million
is a reasonable "round figure." I have found it con-
venient for my purposes to use the total of 2,174 million for the year 1940, since the compilers of *Whitaker's
Almanac*, using data supplied by the United Nations,
have analyzed that total on a continental basis.

World Population Increase

However staggering the figures for the total world population may be, it is the present rapid net increase that
has turned attention to the need of stock-taking of the
world's resources of food, raw materials, and sources
of power.

At first sight this present rapid increase may come as
a surprise. We of the Western world, conscious of the
general practice of birth control, contrast the small
families of today with those of our grandparents or
great-grandparents. We remember, too, the toll of two
world wars in human lives. We are more apt to forget
our increasing control over disease—the number of diseases no longer fatal, the lowering of maternal and in-
fant mortality, and the consequent greater expectation
of life. Queen Anne of England (1665–1714), happily
married and enjoying the best medical skill of the day,
bore seventeen children, only one of whom survived
infancy, and he died at the age of eleven. Such a record
was by no means uncommon two centuries ago. Still
more are we apt to overlook the effect of the develop-

ments in medical science and skill in countries where voluntary limitation of families has not yet become general—where, indeed, social adjustments have not kept pace with the progress of science.

Dr. Julian Huxley, indulging in some fascinating

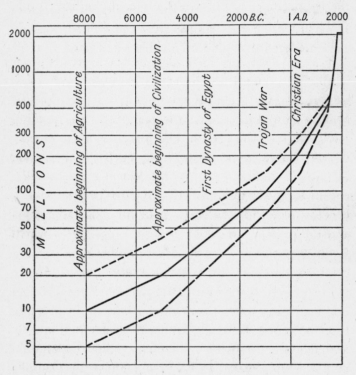

Fig. 1. Graph of world population increase (after Julian S. Huxley). The continuous line indicates the estimated trend of world population for the last 10,000 years; dashed lines represent upper and lower possible limits. Estimates before A.D. 1650 are very rough. No account is taken of possible periods of stagnation or regression in total numbers, which, in any case, would not alter the general character of the curve.

speculation, sees a world total of 3,000 million by 2000 A.D.[1] He arrives at this figure after tracing the world's population growth from a surmised 10 million about 8000 B.C., i.e., at the organized hunting stage, to a present-day figure of 2,200 million. However inaccurate the figures may be in detail, there is no doubt as to the sharp upward trend (see Fig. 1).

Before examining Huxley's startling forecast we must look more closely at present-day trends which are known with some accuracy. By the 1930's in Britain and north-western Europe generally the rate of net increase had been so slowed down that the population was tending towards a stationary level. The forecasts of the demographers have, however, been upset by changes due directly or indirectly to World War II. The sudden rise in the birth rate immediately after the war was to be expected, with the reunion of husbands and wives and the desire to re-establish family life. Births which would normally be spread over a number of years have been concentrated within a short period, giving an abnormally high annual rate. Attempts are being made to get a better perspective on the situation by relating births not to one year but to a woman's reproductive period and thus to the size of "completed" families. Other factors also may be tending to reverse the previous decline in crude birth rates. We think of the effects of national "social security," full employment, and health schemes—surely Britain's "Womb to Tomb" policy of social security must be deemed a failure if it does not restore confidence in the future of the family. It certainly seems to have had this effect, at least temporarily.

If we ignore these postwar changes in western Europe and accept the view that the slower annual rate of increase of under one-half per cent will reestablish itself, this applies to less than one-tenth of all mankind. Let us look at India and Pakistan, which together have one-fifth of all mankind. These two countries illustrate some of the many difficulties in the analysis of population increase. The decennial census figures represent a degree of accuracy high for a territory outside Europe or the English-speaking world. The annual increase for the decade 1931-41 is given as 1.41, yet FAO uses only 1.0 as the figure for 1937-47, and this is the value used in constructing Figure 2. The lower figure is justified by the marked drop in crude birth rates from a peak of 35.4 per one thousand in 1933 to a low of 25.8 in 1944. On

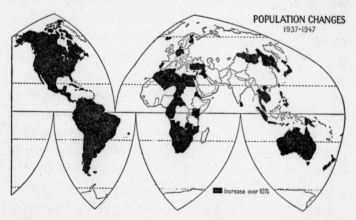

POPULATION CHANGES
1937-1947

■ Increase over 10%

Fig. 2. The new lands of the Americas, Africa, and Australia continue to show the most rapid population changes. (Data from FAO.)

the other hand, the crude death rate ranged from a peak of 24.5 in 1934 to a low of 18.7 in 1946; in 1933 it was 22.1 and in 1944, 24.4. Thus the net gain was 13.3 per one thousand in 1933, but only 1.4 in 1944.

But the absolute figures are still huge. Between 1931-41 the population of India and Pakistan increased by 48,000,000, from 341,000,000 to 389,000,000 persons. In the one year 1933 the increase was about four and three-quarter million against only a little more than half a million in 1944. Such fluctuations reflect the intense crowding and pressure on land and natural resources, with the ever-present danger of famine and consequent death from starvation or the incidence of epidemic diseases and the still imperfect availability of medical services. In the last few years large scale population movements between Moslem Pakistan and Hindu India have added to the confusion.

Nevertheless, we find remarkable fluctuations in the birth rate for even such a country as the United States. There the crude birth rate touched a low of 16.6 per thousand in the depression year of 1933 and climbed to 21.5 in the war-boom year of 1943 and 25.8 in the post-war "family" year of 1947. The death rates ranged from 10.7 in 1933 to a low of 10.0 in 1946, with 10.6 in 1944 and 10.1 in 1947. The net gain in the United States was 5.9 per thousand in 1933 and as much as 15.7 in 1947.

Thus in the postwar family drive Americans were having as many babies as Asiatic Indians who scarcely know the meaning of birth control. Owing to the much higher survival rate, the American population is growing at a far greater rate than India's "teeming millions."

In his forward calculations Huxley uses the estimate that the present rate of world population increase is 1.15 per cent per annum. This means a net addition to the world family of 25,000,000 a year. The population of Australia is added to the world in four months, of Canada in six or seven months, and of the whole United States in six years. It is even more startling when one remembers at breakfast time that there are 70,000 more mouths in the world to be fed than there were on the previous morning! As Huxley points out, we may perhaps have an unexpected fall in the rate of increase in what our town planners call the "foreseeable future" of twenty years, even to one per cent, but at the end of that twenty years the *absolute* daily increase in the number of people would still be greater than it is today.

It will be noted that the figures quoted above from FAO give a world increase of population between mid-1937 and mid-1947 of 171,920,000, that is 17.2 million a year or a rate of 0.8 per cent per annum; the revised figures to mid-1948 give 18.5 million a year, or 0.86 per cent per annum. Even when we use the lower value we still get some staggering figures of net increase. Apart from the incidence of plague or famine of a magnitude the world has never known, or an atomic war of unimaginable destructiveness, we face the inevitability of a huge world population increase year by year in the immediate future. This remains true even if we restrict attention to those countries where trends are accurately known.

Neo-Malthusianism

It was in 1798 that Thomas Robert Malthus published the first edition of *An Essay on the Principle of Population as it affects the Future Improvement of Society*. In later editions the original pamphlet was enlarged into a book and many of the highly original ideas expanded or modified. The fundamental thesis remained that population, if unchecked, increases in a geometrical ratio while subsistence increases only in arithmetical ratio; that population always increases up to the limits of the means of subsistence and is only checked by war, famine, pestilence, and the influence of miseries derived from a consequent low standard of living. Following the fierce controversy aroused by his argument, a century of world expansion with developments of new lands undreamed of by Malthus led to general disparagement of the essay and to the branding of its teaching as completely out of date. Now, once more, the truth of his basic assertion is very much "in date."

Population increase among human beings does not differ essentially from the same process in the biological world generally, and this was the great principle first clearly enunciated by Malthus. With the lessening incidence of the natural checks of famine and pestilence, world population is again pressing on world resources, and this time, in contrast to 1798, there are no longer vast overseas lands awaiting *easy* development.

Table I gives some figures of world population if present trends continue. The starting point is a world population of 2,350,000,000 in the year 1950, and populations are shown according to given annual rates of increase. It should be noted that rates exceeding two per cent are shown by numerous countries such as Argentina and several other South American republics and by the Philippines before the Japanese invasion. Temporary decreases are shown by France and certain European countries devastated by war, but a decreasing population anywhere is still a rare phenomenon. Even France, so often quoted as the example of a long-settled European country where population had passed its peak and was declining, showed a marked increase from 1946 to 1949.

DISTRIBUTION OF POPULATION BY CONTINENTS

So far we have considered the world as a whole. For the position by continents we shall do well to study Table II. This table is surprising in that it refutes the popular belief that the "white" races are being swamped by the "colored"—brown, black, and yellow.[2] In 1940 the predominantly "white" continents had 39.6 per cent of the world's people against 21.1 per cent in 1750. This point is further clarified in Table III, which is concerned only with the present century.

As we should expect, the new lands of North and South America and Australia have shown the most rapid rates of increase in the present century, but what is surprising is the increase in highly populated Europe

TABLE I. FUTURE WORLD POPULATION IN MILLIONS

(calculated at differing rates of net annual increase)*

A. D.	0.25%	0.50%	0.75%	1.00%	1.15%	1.50%
1950	2,350	2,350	2,350	2,350	2,350	2,350
1960	2,409	2,470	2,532	2,596	2,635	2,727
1975	2,501	2,662	2,833	3,014	3,128	3,410
2000	2,662	3,016	3,414	3,865	4,163	4,947
2500	9,278	36,510	143,200	559,500	1,266,000	8,460,000
3000	32,330	442,000	6,003,000	81,000,000	384,800,000	$1,447 \times 10^7$
5000	4,769,000	$9,496 \times 10^6$	$1,856 \times 10^{10}$	$3,558 \times 10^{13}$	$3,289 \times 10^{15}$	$1,237 \times 10^{20}$

The last figure set out in full is: 123,700,000,000,000,000,000

Table prepared by Dr. E. C. Rhodes, Reader in Statistics in the University of London.

* 1.50 per cent per annum, i.e. less than rate in South America, rather over rate in India, 1931–41.
1.15 per cent per annum, estimated world rate, 1920–47; rate for U.S.S.R., 1926–39; far below rate for the U.S.A., 1940–50.
1.00 per cent per annum, rate in Canada, 1931–41, and Australia, 1933–47.
0.75 per cent per annum, just over rate in U.S.A., 1930–40; just under world rate estimated by FAO for 1937–47.
0.50 per cent per annum, rate for England and Wales, 1921–31 and 1931–51.
0.25 per cent per annum, below rate for any important group of countries.

TABLE II. POPULATION OF THE WORLD BY CONTINENTS, 1650–1947*

Numbers in Millions

Continent	1650	1750	1800	1850	1900	1933	1940	1947
Europe	100	140	187	266	401	519	575†	579†
North America	1	1.3	5.7	26	81	137	143	157
C. and S. America	12	11.1	18.9	33	63	125	132	153
Oceania	2	2	2	2	6	10	11	12
Africa	100	95	90	95	120	145	158	191
Asia	330	479	602	749	937	1,121	1,155	1,238
TOTAL	545	728	906	1,171	1,608	2,057	2,174	2,330

Percentage Distribution

Continent	1650	1750	1800	1850	1900	1933	1940	1947
Europe	18.3	19.2	20.7	22.7	24.9	25.2	26.4	24.8
North America	0.2	0.1	0.7	2.3	5.1	6.7	6.6	6.7
C. and S. America	2.2	1.5	2.1	2.8	3.9	6.1	6.1	6.6
Oceania	0.4	0.3	0.2	0.2	0.4	0.5	0.5	0.5
Africa	18.3	13.1	9.9	8.1	7.4	7.0	7.3	8.2
Asia	60.6	65.8	66.4	63.9	58.3	54.5	53.1	53.2
TOTAL	100.0	100.0	100.0	100.0	100.0	100.0	100.0	100.0

* A. M. Carr-Saunders: *World Population*, 1936, p. 42, revising calculations of W. F. Willcox, p. 30. To this have been added the column for 1940 from *Whitaker's Almanac* and the column for 1947 from the *World Population Trends, 1920–47*, United Nations: 1949.

† Including the whole of the U.S.S.R.

over the same period, a rate much higher than in Asia, which actually has the lowest rate of the continents. The European-Asian position is confused, however, by the inclusion in 1940 of all the U.S.S.R. with Europe, so that actually the European rate should be lower and

TABLE III. INCREASE OF POPULATION 1900–40

In millions

	Population 1900	Increase to 1940	Increase per cent	Average per annum
Europe	401	174 (144)	43.4 (35.9)	1.1 (0.9)
North America	81	62	76.5	1.9
C. and S. America	63	69	109.5	2.7
Oceania	6	5	82.5	2.1
Africa	120	38	31.7	0.8
Asia	937	218 (248)	23.3 (26.5)	0.6 (0.7)
WORLD	1,608	566	35.2	0.9

the Asiatic higher. If we allow 30 million of the population of the U.S.S.R. in 1940 to be in Asia and 142 million in Europe, the adjusted figures are those shown in parentheses. The position of Africa also is surprising—next to Asia at the bottom of the table.

In considering the figures for Europe, one must recall the appalling slaughter of World War I; but Asia over the same period suffered the unprecedented death toll of the influenza epidemic of 1917-19 when 18,000,-000 died in India alone.

CRUDE DENSITIES

The preceding section suggests the irregularity of population distribution as well as differential rates of population increase. To get a broad picture of distribution, we may first consider crude densities by continents and by political units.

Excluding Antarctica as uninhabited and uninhabitable in the foreseeable future, the land area of the world is calculated at 51,375,000 square miles, or 32,880,000,000 acres. Using the world population figure of 1940, the average density is 42 persons to a square mile, or one person to 15 acres.[3]

The population densities of Australia and New Zealand, South America, North America, Africa, and the vast territories of the U.S.S.R. are all well below the world average. The density in North America is only half the world average, whereas in Asia, excluding Russia, the density at 115 a square mile is nearly three times the world average; in Europe at 200 to the square mile it is five times the world average.

An attempt has been made in Figure 3 to deal with crude densities by political units. In Europe only Sweden, Norway, and Finland, together with Iceland, fall below 42 per square mile or the world average. The highest figures are shown by England and Wales, followed by the Netherlands, Belgium, and parts of Germany.

Among the larger countries of Asia, population densities are extremely high in Java, but that is the only country which approaches in population concentration the more densely populated parts of Europe. The danger of dealing with crude densities is illustrated at once by the figures for China and India, where the prevalence

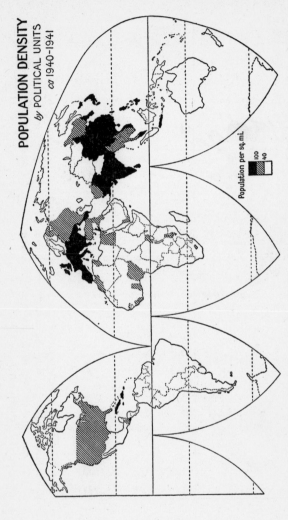

POPULATION DENSITY
by POLITICAL UNITS
ca 1940-1941

Population per sq. mi.

100
40

Fig. 3. The most populous countries are not generally the areas of most rapid population increase. (See Figure 2.)

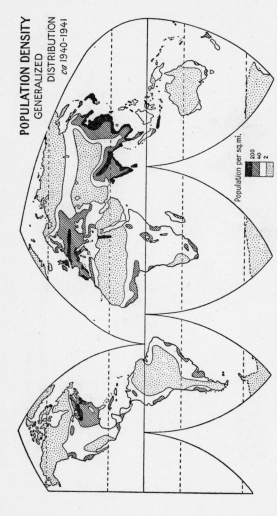

POPULATION DENSITY
GENERALIZED
DISTRIBUTION
ca 1940-1941

Population per sq.mi.

200
40
2

Fig. 4. A more accurate picture of the world's population is obtained by disregarding political units and plotting the actual distribution of people. The concentrations on the alluvial soils of Asia and in the industrialized areas of Europe and eastern North America are especially conspicuous.

of large stretches of mountainous and arid land leads to an overall density which is only moderate, though the cultivated lowlands of those countries are among the most densely peopled areas on earth.

Similarly the limitations of crude density figures are illustrated from the United States, just about 42 persons per square mile, and Canada, with an average density of only three. To counteract the false impressions thus created, Figure 4 shows broadly the realities of distribution of people over the earth's surface. The shaded areas all have a density greater than world average of 42 (the black areas more than 200 per square mile). The lightly dotted areas are virtually uninhabited —less than 2 persons per square mile.

POPULATION OF THE PRINCIPAL COUNTRIES

Only about fifteen countries today have a known population of more than 20 million. In order they are China, the Republic of India, the U.S.S.R., the United States, Japan, Pakistan, Germany, Great Britain, Brazil, Italy, France, Spain, Korea, Poland, and Mexico. In some of these countries, notably China, very little is known of the composition of the population, but in others regular censuses have been taken for some time past. We can use them to illustrate the remarkable difference between such "old lands" as India and Pakistan, Japan, England and Wales, and France on the one hand, and such "new lands" as Canada, the United States, Australia, and Israel on the other.

Figs. 5-6. Diagrams of age-composition of the population of Britain in 1891 and 1947. The length of each bar indicates the percentage of the total population in each age group (ages 0-4, 5-9, 10-14, 15-19, etc.).

CONTRASTS IN AGE STRUCTURE

The "fir-tree" diagrams, Figures 5 and 6, illustrate the age composition of the population of Great Britain and its changed character in just over a half-century. The diagram for 1891 is typical of an expanding population,

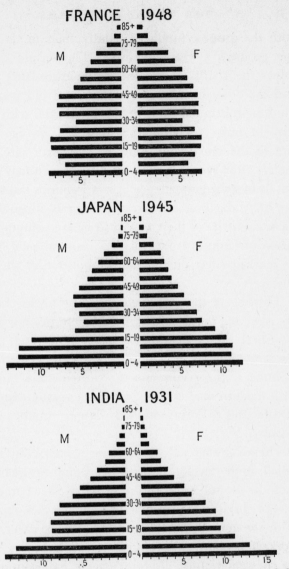

Figs. 7-9. Diagrams of age-composition of other countries of the Old World.

with the greatest number of individuals in the lowest age group, 0-4 years inclusive. The second diagram shows the results of the increasing expectancy of life and the consequent greater number of old people, of the long-continued drop in the birth rate, with a consequent bulge of population in the 35-39 age group, and of the remarkable jump in the birth rate immediately after World War II, a feature which may or may not be of some permanence. Apart from this last feature, the 1947 diagram for Great Britain is illustrative of those countries of the Old World where voluntary limitation of families from whatever cause already has had its marked effect on the age composition of the population.

Turning to the corresponding diagram for India in 1931, we see the demographic characteristics of a country where the population is rapidly expanding, notably the large numbers of children. A similar general trend is shown in the diagram for the United States, but there, with modern medical skill, we find a greater expectancy of life and a correspondingly larger number of old people.

The diagrams tell an interesting story. In the so-called underdeveloped lands work falls primarily on those in the full vigor of the prime of life. Large numbers of children absorb much of the energies, especially of the women, but children are needed to carry on the work. Too many old people may form a serious burden on the community. If, for example, we consider the working population to be mainly between the ages of

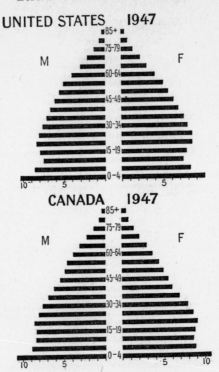

Figs. 10-11. Diagrams of age-composition in two new lands.

20 and 64 inclusive, the support of those of age 65 and over is an increasing burden, though with the lower birth rate and the smaller number of children there are fewer youthful dependents. Direct comparisons between countries are difficult for many reasons. In the underdeveloped countries it may be presumed that adolescents have become members of the working population long before reaching the age of twenty whereas in Western countries many at that age are still in college.

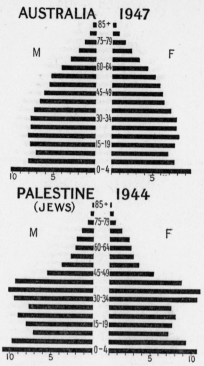

Figs. 12-13. Diagrams of age-composition in other new lands.

The 1947 diagram for Great Britain suggests the disadvantage to the country of an emigration policy which would still further lower the numbers of younger wage earners but leave the same number of over-age dependents (Fig. 14). That whole sections of the population, including the elderly, should emigrate has been recognized by some recipient countries; for example, in recent years British emigrants to Australia have been officially encouraged to take their parents with them, and to trans-

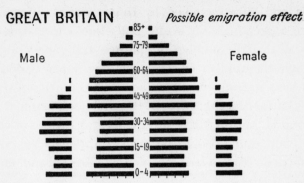

GREAT BRITAIN   *Possible emigration effect*

Male   Female

Fig. 14. Diagram showing possible effect of large-scale emigration on the British population. If the migration were of young people as shown by the detached parts, the population left behind would be hopelessly overbalanced by the aged.

fer whole families. It is still true, however, in the majority of immigrant countries that only the young and the young workers find a welcome, unless the older people can bring capital and are independent. Emigration from the over-crowded European countries may create as many problems as it solves. On the other hand remittances from emigrant children to their parents in the home land, such as dollar remittances from America to Greece and Italy, may play a large part in balancing trade.

In Figure 15, we have distinguished between children and adolescents (0-19), persons of "working" age (20-64), and over-age dependents (those of 65 and over). The old countries of northwestern Europe are characterized by a very large proportion of over-age dependents, a large working population, and a relatively small number of young people (Group I). In Group II are countries of

Asia and Africa typified by India and Egypt, which have a very high birth rate but a low expectation of life, so that the number of children and young people is high, the number of old people low. Japan is similar but has a greater life expectancy. The countries of tropical Latin America (Group III) are not dissimilar to Group II, but they have still higher proportions of children and young people. Group IV represents the "new countries" of mid-latitudes—fewer children and more

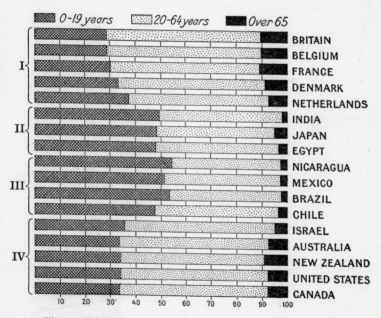

Fig. 15. Diagram summarizing the age-composition of the population of selected countries from four groups: I, the old settled countries of northwestern Europe; II, countries of Asia and Africa; III, Latin American countries; IV, "new countries" of mid-latitudes.

old people, but with fewer old people than in Group I. Chile, it will be noticed, has an intermediate position. Table IV summarizes the situation for the world as a whole and for its regions, but using age 60 and over.

TABLE IV. ESTIMATED WORLD POPULATION BY AGE GROUPS*
Numbers in millions and percentages, 1947

	Under 15		15 to 59		60 and over	
	Nos.	%	Nos.	%	Nos.	%
Africa	76	40	105	55	10	5
Anglo-America	39	25	101	64	17	11
Latin-America	61	40	84	55	8	5
Asia	493	40	685	55	60	5
Near East	30	40	40	54	4	6
South Central	170	40	239	56	17	4
Japan	29	37	44	55	6	8
Rest of Far East	264	40	362	55	33	5
Europe						
North, West, Central	50	24	130	62	30	14
Southern	27	30	52	59	10	11
Eastern and U.S.S.R.	95	34	165	59	20	7
Oceania	3	28	8	62	1	10
WORLD TOTALS	844	36	1,330	57	156	7

* World Population Trends, 1920–1947.

SOME CONTRASTS BETWEEN RACES

The diagrams and figures in the preceding sections reveal marked contrasts between population trends in one country and another. Is it possible to draw any distinctions, at least on a broad basis, between different peoples? The problem posed is fraught with difficulties, and few studies have been attempted. The German geographer Friedrich Burgdörfer [4] essayed a brief survey of the position as between Europeans and non-Europeans. Carr-Saunders in summarizing changes between 1650 and 1930 noted that the brown and yellow peoples had clearly made large actual gains with the likelihood that they had about maintained their proportion of world population. The black peoples had suffered heavy relative losses; from having once formed about one-fifth the population of the world they now formed but one-fifteenth. It was the white peoples who gained most—from about 100,000,000 to 720,000,000, or nearly double the rate of growth for the peoples of the world as a whole. But what of the present and the immediate future?

Is it, for example, true that the white peoples today show a slowing down of population expansion, whereas it is now the turn of the Negro population of Africa to show the most marked increases? There is a growing consciousness of the possibilities of the situation, and those who have followed certain Negro literature will know of the arguments for "absorbing the world's white minority." The figures showing the growth of the "white" continents, given above, clearly do not bear out this contention as yet, whatever the future may hold.

The position of the English-speaking white peoples has recently been examined by C. B. Fawcett.[5] He estimated that English-speaking whites numbered 20.3 million in 1800–01 (15.9 million in the British Isles; 4.3 million in the United States) compared with 188 million in 1940–41 (119 million in the United States; 51 million in the British Isles; 9 million in Australia and New Zealand; 8 million in Canada). By 1950 the total had risen to 206 million (if we presume recent immigrants into America are to be classed as "English-speaking"): United Kingdom, 50 million; Eire, 3 million; Australia, 8 million; New Zealand, 2 million; South Africa, 1 million; Canada (with Newfoundland), 9 million; United States, 133 million. Thus nearly 9 per cent of the people of the world are English-speaking whites. They have increased tenfold in the past century and a half, or four times as rapidly as the world's peoples as a whole.

ONE WORLD—OR SEVERAL?

The foregoing considerations make evident how very different are population trends and consequent problems in different parts of the world. Theoretically we may talk about "one great world family" and discuss the increasing pressure of population on world resources. Is this in fact a practical viewpoint? Even assuming an increasing sense of responsibility on the part of the great powers, how far is any one of them justified in going to the aid of those lands where population pressure is in the main the result of a *laissez faire* policy of population growth?

Those who criticize the present political regime in Great Britain, and the confessed object of creating a welfare state, argue that the lower income groups are dragging down the whole nation to their level, with serious cultural and material loss. Others argue that the "leveling" is designed to eliminate poverty, to give all an opportunity in life, and to raise the general standard. We can apply these same contrasted points of view to the visualizing of a world welfare state. In seeking to raise standards of living in the vast overpopulated lands, and in seeking to develop the underdeveloped lands, does it follow that there will be a lowering of present standards in the world's leading nations? If famine in India or China or Africa is to be explained primarily by population pressure resulting from the working of Malthusian principles, should the Western nations be compelled to accept such a position or should their help be contingent upon conscious efforts by, let us say, Eastern nations and Africa to change social conditions? If United States aid to the underdeveloped countries is thus made conditionally, then this is dictation and a new form of imperialism. The dangers inherent in such power are obvious.

CHAPTER III

The World's Lands

The surface of the globe, both land and water, has been calculated to be 196,836,000 square miles. Of this total only a little more than one-quarter, or 55,786,000 square miles, is land. Distribution by continents, in square miles, is thus: Europe (including European Russia), 4,093,000; Asia (including Asiatic Russia), 16,677,000; Africa, 11,699,000; North America (including Central), 8,658,000; South America, 7,047,000; Oceania, 3,201,000; Antarctica, 4,411,000. The British Commonwealth (1950) ranks first in area with about 14 million square miles, the U.S.S.R. is second with 8 1/3 million square miles, followed by France and the French Union (1939) with 4 1/3 million, the United States with 3 3/4 million, Brazil with 3 1/4 million, and China with 3 million. Here figures of area have, of course, little meaning. We are concerned with those parts of the earth's surface which are permanently settled by human beings, or which can be made habitable.

The Habitable Globe

Much of the land of the globe is not suited for human habitation. Geographers are accustomed to refer to "negative areas"—that is, areas which are, broadly, uninhabited and in many cases are likely to remain empty. What are the chief factors responsible for this negative character?

In the first place we may eliminate the areas permanently covered by ice and snow. Apart from Antarctica there is the great Greenland ice cap, covering such a large proportion of that lofty island that only small tracts around the fringes are ice-free. There are also huge areas where the snow cover may disappear for a short period but which are beyond the possibility of normal human settlement. A large part of northern Canada and the associated Arctic islands fall in this category. We have only recently begun to study the permafrost zone—that is, the areas where the heat of summer is insufficient to do more than thaw the surface layers and where the soil or subsoil is permanently frozen at depth. The permafrost areas in Canada, Alaska, and the U.S.S.R. are estimated to cover some five million square miles, which, with Antarctica and Greenland, comprise one-fifth of the world's land surface. Even outside the permafrost zone there are large areas where the growing season is too short for crop cultivation, though sparse settlement dependent on pastoral occupation or fishing may be possible.

We can eliminate large areas of highland, too rugged or too lofty to permit settlement depending on cultivation. In total, certainly more than another fifth of the earth's surface falls in this category.

There are large areas where precipitation is insuffi-

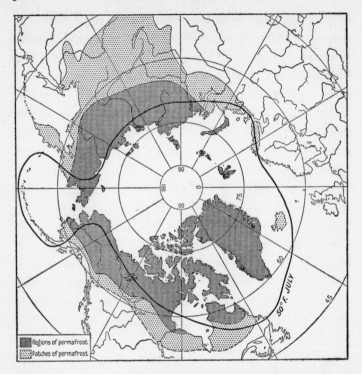

Fig. 16. The cold lands of the northern hemisphere. This map shows the ice-cap areas, where permanent settlement is obviously impossible, and the permafrost areas of permanently frozen subsoil where agriculture in the ordinarily accepted sense may be regarded as impossible; the same is true over most of the huge tracts where permafrost occurs in patches. Older authorities have regarded the July isotherm of 50° F. as marking the northern limit of possible cultivation. North of this line grazing on "arctic prairies" by reindeer and other animals is possible, but only small populations could be supported.

This map, not previously published, was specially prepared by Professor F. Kenneth Hare, McGill University, Montreal, based on the work of Sumgin (U.S.S.R.), Müller (Alaska), Jenness (Canada west of Hudson Bay), and Hare (east of Hudson Bay).

cient to support more than the scantiest vegetation—the deserts or arid regions. Where water is available from underground sources or from rivers arising in adjacent humid lands, irrigation may permit settlement; but over huge areas there is no such possibility, and almost certainly another fifth of the earth's surface can be eliminated on grounds of aridity, at least with methods of watering now at our command. Except in the rarest cases, the occurrence of minerals of economic importance is not conditioned by climate, and mining settlements may be and are found in areas where settlement would otherwise be ruled out.

If we regard the habitable lands as those having physical and climatic conditions permitting the growth of crops desired by man, the area available does not cover more than two-fifths of the land surface. Even then,

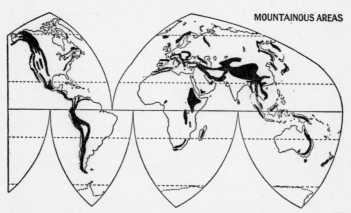

MOUNTAINOUS AREAS

Fig. 17. The main areas where the rugged or extremely elevated character of the surface prohibits close settlement are very roughly shown.

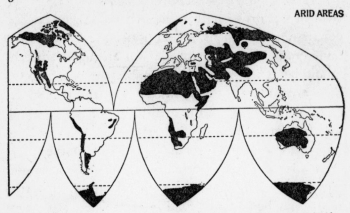

ARID AREAS

Fig. 18. This map shows where rainfall or other precipitation is too small to allow close agricultural settlement without irrigation. Roughly, the areas shown in black have less than 10 inches of rain or equivalent in snow in middle or high latitudes and less than 20 inches of rain in the tropics.

much more must be eliminated because of the absence or poverty of soil or because of excessive rainfall.

Excluding Antarctica, a present-day world population of 2,350,000,000 means an allotment of about 14 acres a head, or an average density of 46 persons a square mile (18 a square kilometer). As soon, however, as we start eliminating the other "negative" areas, the figure of 14 acres a head is greatly reduced.

HABITABLE AND INHABITED AREAS

The optimists are fond of pointing to the fact that there are huge areas of the earth's surface, apparently well watered, supporting a luxuriant or at least an adequate natural vegetation, but which at the present day are either sparsely populated or almost uninhabited. The

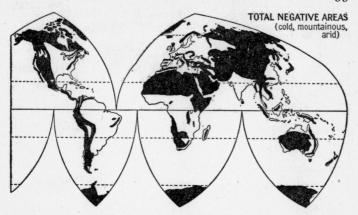

TOTAL NEGATIVE AREAS
(cold, mountainous, arid)

Fig. 19. The map combines Figures 16, 17, and 18 and shows those parts of the earth's surface which through cold, aridity, or mountainous character prohibit close settlement and agricultural development. It does not take account of irrigation settlements where the "negative" character of the land has been counteracted, notably in Egypt, Iraq, north-western India and Western Pakistan, Russian Central Asia, and parts of western United States.

The blank areas which remain on this map are potentially cultivable or actually cultivated. Although so much of the earth's surface has been eliminated, many areas have been given the benefit of the doubt in deciding whether or not they are "cultivable": thus, the high plateau of Bolivia, a considerable part of the Canadian Shield, Finland, and the Russian forest lands are included.

The map serves to focus attention on the "positive" or presumably developable areas of South America and Africa as the major underdeveloped lands, and calls attention to comparable problems of Canada and U.S.S.R. in northward expansion.

outstanding example is, of course, the great Amazon basin of South America—some two million square miles. If for a moment we regard these tracts as "habitable" we see that there is a marked contrast between the habitable and the actually inhabited areas of the earth.

A number of years ago Professor C. B. Fawcett [1] came to the conclusion that the extent of the cultivable land of the earth was 30 per cent of the total land area, that is about 16 million square miles. Insofar as permanent settlement depends on cultivation, this is equivalent to saying habitable area. He noted that another 30 per cent might be classed as productive but not cultivable—forest and poor grazing land, with mountain and hill pastures, semiarid ranch and bush—but the remainder (40 per cent) he estimated as occupied by the deserts, dry and cold. The wet forested lands of the hot belt he included in the cultivable lands as the regions offering the chief possibilities for extension of cultivation.

By contrast with the cultivable areas, equivalent to 10,000 million acres or a little more than four acres a head of population, the actual cultivated lands occupy between 3,000 and 4,000 million acres, let us say one-and-a-half acres a head of population. A recent estimate of world land use by FAO is given in Table V, with figures converted into acres and square miles.

TABLE V. WORLD LAND-USE*

In millions

	Acres	sq. mls.	Per cent
Arable or cropped	3,006	4.7	9.1
Meadow and permanent pasture	5,269	8.2	15.9
Forest and woodland	8,702	13.6	26.3
Unused but potentially productive	936	1.5	2.8
Built over, wasteland, and other	15,200	23.7	45.9
TOTAL	33,113	51.7	100.0

* *Yearbook of Food and Agricultural Statistics, 1949.*

Dr. Hugh H. Bennett [2] quotes a figure of "two-and-a-half acres per capita of reasonably productive land" as

necessary to produce "even a minimum adequate diet."
On this basis, if all the supposedly "cultivable" lands of
the world could actually be brought into use, there
would be a margin for the present world population,
but not for the increased population of a few decades
hence. On the other hand, the actual cultivated area of
the world falls far short of providing the calculated minimum. We now begin to get a measure of population
pressure on land resources.

When we examine the distribution of the actually
cultivated land we find it to be very different from that
of the land just called "cultivable." We are tempted to
see therein vast areas underdeveloped and awaiting utilization. How can the validity of such an idea be tested?
A first approach is through consideration of the world's
climates.

CLIMATIC REGIONS OF THE WORLD

A number of different classifications have been proposed for climatic regions.[3] Into these I shall not enter
here; suffice it to say that for my present purpose I make
use primarily of the classification of Finch and Trewartha in the slightly modified form in which it appears
in the *Army Service Forces Manual M 101*. This classification has the advantage of being in close agreement
with Professor A. J. Herbertson's well-known regional
scheme. As will be seen by a comparison of Figures 20
and 21, Finch and Trewartha's Type A1, Tropical Rainforest, is the same as Herbertson's Equatorial but has
been extended by Type 1t to include the wettest parts
of the Tropical Climate of Herbertson and by 1m to

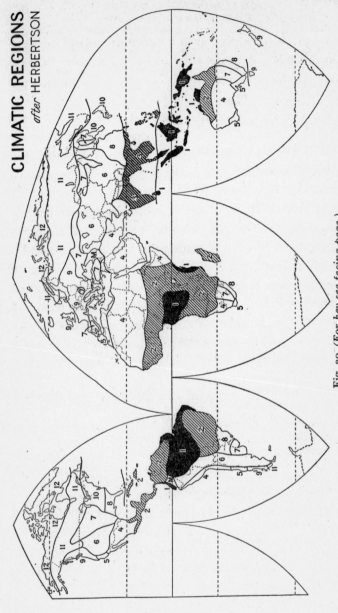

CLIMATIC REGIONS
after HERBERTSON

Fig. 20. (*For key see facing page.*)

include the wettest parts of Tropical Monsoon lands. Type A2, Tropical Savanna, is the same as Herbertson's Tropical together with Tropical Monsoon of India and southeast Asia, and so Types 1 and 2 of Finch and Trewartha are particularly the "underdeveloped" areas with which we are concerned.

EQUATORIAL CLIMATE OR TROPICAL RAINFOREST

As its name implies, this is the type of climate normally found as a belt stretching some five to ten degrees on either side of the equator. It is the region where constant heat throughout the year results in continuous evaporation, upward movement of air currents, and local rather than regional winds. Temperatures are not extreme; over huge areas the thermometer rarely drops below 70° F. and rarely rises above 90° F. The mean for every day of the year is not far from 80° F. Just as monotony is the keynote of temperature, so it is of rainfall. In many parts the early morning mist suggests a cool-

Fig. 20 (*opposite*). The climatic-vegetation regions of the world, after A. J. Herbertson.

Low-latitude or Tropical Zone Climates
1 Equatorial or hot, wet
2 Tropical or Sudan type
3 Monsoon or summer rain
4 Hot desert or Sahara type

Mid-latitude or Temperate Zone Climates
5 Mediterranean or winter rain
6 Mid-latitude desert or Iran type

7 Mid-latitude continental or grassland
8 Humid subtropical or warm temperate east coast
9 Cool temperate oceanic or rain at all seasons
10 Humid continental or cool east coast

Cold Climates
11 Subarctic or boreal forest
12 Arctic or cold desert

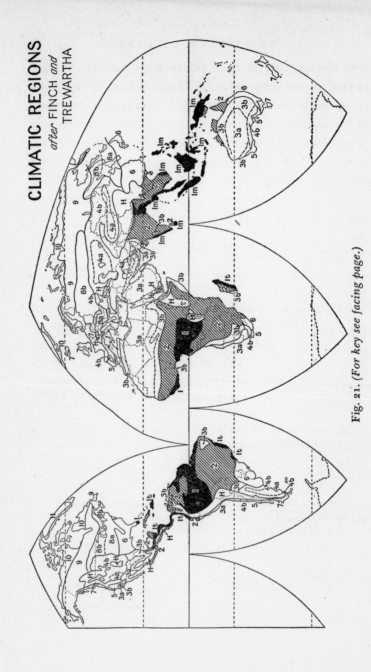

CLIMATIC REGIONS

after FINCH *and* TREWARTHA

Fig. 21. *(For key see facing page.)*

ness more apparent than real, and the mist is soon dispersed by morning sunshine. Evaporation is rapid, ascending air currents frequently result in the formation of clouds in the afternoon, followed by a heavy downpour of rain, the sky clearing again in the late evening.

Such a daily regime may be repeated almost without variation throughout the year, though in some places one season may be wetter than another and in other places a double rainfall maximum in the course of the year is normal. The rainfall is always adequate—80 inches is a typical average—is always in marked excess of evaporation, and is not subject to violent fluctuations from year to year.

The keynote of the equatorial climate is thus a combination of heat and moisture and an absence of seasonal rhythm. These conditions are reflected in the nat-

Fig. 21 (*opposite*). The climatic regions of the world, after V. C. Finch and G. T. Trewartha.

A *Tropical Rainy Climates*
   1 Tropical Rainforest
     1t Windward Coasts
     1m Monsoon type
   2 Tropical savanna

B *Dry Climates*
   3 Low-latitude dry
     3a Low-latitude desert
     3b Low-latitude steppe
   4 Mid-latitude dry
     4a Mid-latitude desert

H *Undifferentiated Highlands*

C *Humid Mesothermal Climates*
   5 Mediterranean
   6 Humid subtropical
   7 Marine west coast

D *Humid Microthermal Climates*
   8 Humid continental
     8a Long-summer phase
     8b Short-summer phase
   9 Subarctic

E *Polar Climates*
   10 Tundra
   11 Ice cap

ural vegetation, typically a lofty, evergreen forest. Individual trees may and do have their resting periods and may shed their leaves, but there is no period when the forest as a whole displays the typical features of a resting period such as that in the deciduous forest of mid-latitudes. Heat and moisture induce continuous and easy growth, trees grow tall and unbranched in their struggle for existence; other plants have adopted the habits of woody climbers and epiphytes, living high up on the supporting trees. Much of the animal life of these forests also is concentrated in the treetops. By contrast the floor of the forest is commonly in perpetual gloom, littered with a debris of fallen leaves which decay with a damp, fetid odor rather than change to the humus associated with mid-latitudes.

Over huge areas the equatorial lands are scarcely to be described as underdeveloped. They are literally undeveloped and largely uninhabited. At first sight this may seem difficult to explain. In a wood-hungry world, why should these forests, which afford the largest stretches of unworked timber land, have remained so little exploited? The trees are of many different species; the majority, though not all, are hardwoods of the type known technically as "tropical cabinet woods." These are of somewhat limited use; indeed less than two per cent of the timber consumed in the world is to be described under the general title of tropical hardwood. Each wood is distinctive and while there is a commercial demand for a few types, it is difficult to establish a demand for all. Consequently, in exploitation, the alternatives are clear felling of the forest with the difficulty of finding a market or indeed a use for the many and varied types of timber, or selective felling of the commercially valuable trees, a virtually impossible task.

Since we are chiefly concerned at this time with the provision of food for the growing human family, we should perhaps look at the equatorial forest from the point of view of the value of the cleared land.

The admittedly luxuriant growth of the giant trees has led to some false assessments of the value of the land when cleared. The deduction that the soil must be inherently fertile has proved repeatedly to be far from the truth. With rainfall always in excess of evaporation, there is a net downward movement of water in the soil. That is to say, there is downward leaching which, when the soils are exposed, tends to impoverish the surface layers and to sweep plant food downwards, leaving the surface a sterile mixture of mineral particles. At the same time, when the forest is cleared and the soil exposed, the high temperatures induce rapid chemical action, notably rapid oxidation. The resultant impoverishment of the soil is increased rapidly by the process of plowing. We may literally say, as was proved from experiments many years ago in Ceylon, that the goodness can be plowed out of the soil in a very short time. By and large, if cleared, the equatorial forests would provide vast areas of poor or indifferent soils, liable to become still further impoverished, and further liable to marked soil erosion.

The old myth that equatorial soils are of great fertility dies hard. Early writers on Ceylon, for example J. W. Bennett in *Ceylon and its Capabilities* (1843), refer repeatedly to its "fertile soil," "preeminent in natural resources"; but Sir Samuel Baker in a work we shall have occasion to mention later, speaks of his disillusionment as a pioneer of 1848 when he says: [4]

"The appearance of the [soil] has deceived everyone, especially the black soil of the patina, which my bailiff on his first arrival declared to be excellent. Lord Torrington, who is well-known as an agriculturalist, was equally deceived. He was very confident in the opinion that 'it only required draining to enable it to produce anything.' The real fact is that it will not pay for the working. . . . In fact, nothing will permanently succeed in Ceylon soil without abundance of manure, with the exception of cinnamon and cocoa-nuts . . .

"Can any man when describing the 'fertility' of Ceylon be aware that . . . newly-cleared forest land will only produce one crop of the miserable grain called korrakan."

Going back much further, the Amazon basin was the reputed location of El Dorado. Carvajal, who accompanied Orellana on his pioneer journey down its main stream in the sixteenth century, felt compelled to write enthusiastically of the imaginary cities he had hoped to see but did not find. Yet apparently his accounts are accepted at their face value even today by some writers; at least this is the impression conveyed by Earl Hanson in his *New Worlds Emerging*. Even if we accepted these old accounts as literally true, the fact remains that nature has proved the master and destroyed former settlements and civilizations almost without trace.

Two phrases that have been applied to the hot, wet equatorial lands are pregnant with meaning. Professor H. J. Fleure described them as "regions of lasting difficulty," where man was in a state of constant struggle against the natural climatic factors. The second phrase rightly describes the equatorial climate as a "good servant but a bad master."

So far we have referred to the equatorial belt in broad terms; actually there are great contrasts between its different parts. In vast stretches of Amazonian forest small groups of aboriginal tribes eke out a precarious existence, partly by living on or along the waterways and combining fishing with hunting and the gathering of fruits and roots. In the Congo forests there still are primitive groups which emulate the wild animals by living in dwellings in the trees themselves. On the other hand, in some parts, perhaps best exemplified on the margins of the true equatorial belt in Africa, man has succeeded in modifying his environment to some extent. On patches of cleared land where, in part by reason of their small size, soil erosion is kept in check, yams and other vegetables and bananas and other fruits are grown. It is in some of these areas that the cash crop of cocoa has been introduced, as well as the oil palm, and other products of interest in international trade such as sago and tapioca.

Then there are equatorial areas where man can claim to be master. We think particularly of Java, and certain of the favored parts of the East Indies and of the Malayan Peninsula. The food crop of paramount importance is rice, and we notice at once that its cultivation demands special soil conditions: the soil must be such, clay, for example, that it can be worked into a water-holding layer, and the land must either be flat or susceptible of terracing. In Java these conditions are not only fulfilled over considerable areas, but the volcanic soils widespread in the island have a naturally high nutrient status. The developed parts of southeast Asia are also favored by such local modifications that the climate is not typically equatorial. Monsoonal conditions exist, and the seasonal winds, the land and sea breezes, and the varied relief result in pronounced local differences.

The nonfood crop which has meant so much to the development of these lands is the introduced *Hevea brasiliensis,* the rubber tree, and the modern rubber plantations illustrate well the precautions needed when dealing with equatorial lands. It is unwise to clear extensive areas of hillside—great scars all too frequently evidence the danger of exposing the soil to erosion. Even the gently sloping lowlands must be treated with caution. When the forest is cleared, the stumps of the trees are usually left, the roots helping to bind the soil together, and each little rubber tree is rimmed around to prevent rapid runoff; or more commonly the ground is immediately protected by a cover crop, and one which will add to its nutrient status. Protect the soil, keep it covered, is the universal rule in these lands.

However, examined in detail, the conquest of these more favored equatorial lands is far from complete. Less than one-sixth of Malaya, for instance, is under cultivation—food and plantation crops. The cleared valleys and lowlands are separated by large stretches of forest that vie with any in the world for impenetrability.

We may summarize the position in the equatorial lands by saying that the maps suggest that there are at least a couple of million square miles of underdeveloped or undeveloped land; but the difficulties of bringing them into use are enormous and are likely to remain enormous. There is first the difficulty of clearing the land. There is then the difficulty of conserving and building up the soils—a wholly new technique of soil management needs to be developed. Although some important advances are being made, the British expert committee on problems of mechanization,[5] reporting in 1949, failed to reach definite conclusions and the failure of the Groundnut Scheme (described below) was largely due to difficulties of soil management. The third difficulty is the lack of population. While the old idea that these hot, wet lands are unhealthy by reason of their climate is no longer to be accepted in its crude form, the climate does present serious obstacles. Its monotony is incompatible with the normal rhythm of life with its alternating periods of rest and activity. We sum this up by saying that when a man gets run down or below par, recovery is difficult without a change of climate. Further, though the climate itself may not be "unhealthy," there are many widespread diseases—such as yellow fever, malaria, dengue, typhus, dysentery—which take their toll, if not of life, certainly of efficiency.

What are the products to be obtained from equatorial lands? Undoubtedly the chief is rice, but the swing of the world's people, even in those countries where it is grown, is away from rice consumption to the cereals of mid-latitudes, which at present at least cannot be produced in the hot, wet lands. Insofar as these under-developed lands can produce a surplus for export, what should that surplus be?

Some new and alarming pests and diseases of plants have appeared. The recent spread of the swollen shoot disease which threatened for a time to extirpate the cocoa trees and the cocoa industry in West Africa (though it is now believed under control) is an illustration of the disasters besetting development in equatorial lands.

Vast tracts of the equatorial lands may be listed for possible future development, but sober appraisal will insist that the development cannot be undertaken until far more is known of ways to go about it. An appreciation of this fact is UNESCO's creation of the Hylea Research Institute in equatorial Brazil. The establishment of an agronomic institute for the Belgian Congo (INÉAC), with its central field station at Yangambi, is another example of the growth of scientific research in an equatorial land. And most significant for African development are the regular conferences now held by workers in such fields as soils, agronomy, and land use on a pan-African basis.[6] On still broader lines was the first

African Regional Scientific Conference which met at Johannesburg in 1949. The conference passed a resolution creating a Scientific Council for Africa south of the Sahara [7] and this is now being implemented.

THE TROPICAL CLIMATE OR TROPICAL SAVANNA X

We may understand by the term "tropical climate" that which occurs outside the equatorial belt but still within the tropics. It is marked by a distinctive seasonal rhythm, in which it is usual to distinguish three seasons. There is the cool dry season, "cool" having, however, a relative meaning in that the thermometer does not sink below the crucial 43° F., the temperature below which the majority of plants of economic importance cease to be vegetatively active. In general this season, in the northern hemisphere from late October through January to February, is one of sunny skies and, over large areas, of cool, constant winds, since this is the Trade Wind belt. The cool dry season passes gradually into the hot dry season. The land heats up, temperatures by day and night rise, air movement becomes less marked, rain is absent, everything becomes dry and parched. Towards the end of the season many native trees and shrubs, seemingly able to anticipate the coming of the rains, burst into flower before pollination is inhibited. The third season is the hot wet period, often called the rains, from about the end of May or June through September into October, a season when rains are heavy though sometimes spasmodic in their occurrence. It will be noticed that because the rains coincide with what in mid-latitudes would be called the summer, vegetative growth is very active in common with chemical action in the soils.

Though we refer to the tropical climate we might more correctly talk about the tropical climates, in that there is a wide range from the wet margins bordering on equatorial lands where the "dry" season is dry by comparison rather than in actuality, to the arid margins which fade into the great deserts, where the total rainfall for the year is 20 inches or less. These great variations are reflected in the natural vegetation. On the wet equatorial margins the rainfall, though it may be mainly in the one season, is sufficiently heavy (80 inches or more) to maintain the growth of an evergreen forest similar to that of the equatorial lands themselves. Over the vast extent of the tropical lands, however, the vegetation is that variously described as savanna, parkland, orchard-bush, grassland with scattered trees, or locally by such names as campos (Brazil), llanos (Venezuela) and scrub forest.

The tropical climate is *par excellence* the climate of Africa. Over vast stretches are grasslands with scattered trees, such as various species of Acacia and the well-known baobab, which merge into actual forests where water conditions improve, as in the so-called gallery forests along the river valleys. Where conditions are more arid, the trees, often of the same species, become spiny bushes, and there is a natural transition into thorn scrub. Over certain tracts trees and shrubs may be entirely absent; but it would be wrong to think of these vast stretches of grassland in terms of those familiar in mid-latitudes. Tropical grasses not infrequently reach eight and ten feet in height.

Of all the underdeveloped or undeveloped lands in the world the tropical savannas call most urgently for careful study. The term grassland suggests natural pastures awaiting the herdsman. This is what the Spaniards thought when they introduced European cattle into the llanos of the Orinoco basin three centuries ago. How is it that with all the developments in the New World so little use has yet been made of the vast South American pasture lands?

For a first explanation, let us follow the fate of a herd of cattle through the year. The end of a dry season of six to eight months finds them completely exhausted from the constant effort to find water and nutriment in the vast stretches of parched and dried-up grassland. With the first coming of the rains the grass roots spring into life, fodder becomes abundant, and those cattle still able to stand find plenty of sustenance, though, of course, the rains may be delayed, and more animals succumb; and doubtless some overeat and die as a result of the new abundance. For a few weeks the food supply is satisfactory, but so rapid is the vegetative growth that the grasses quickly become tough and lose their palatability and some of their nutritive value. If the rains are heavy, the herd may be in danger of drowning and will have difficulty in finding patches of dry land and spots where young and palatable fodder still exists. The rains last for two or three months, and then the cycle starts over again. We may sum it up by saying that from the point of view of cattle-rearing, the favorable season is about two months out of the twelve.

What then of cultivation? Tropical soils present many problems. In the rainy season heat and moisture combine to cause downward leaching so long as rainfall exceeds evaporation. With the coming of the dry season, the movement of soil moisture is reversed, evaporation exceeds rainfall, the evaporating moisture leaves behind in the soil the salts contained in solution, with the result that a hardpan may be formed at or near the surface. The hardpan in its turn prevents both proper circulation of water in the soil and the penetration of roots. The net result is that tropical soils call for a completely different system of management from that used in mid-latitudes.

To the catalogue of difficulties must be added rainfall variability, which is particularly marked in the drier parts of the tropical lands. An average rainfall of 20 to 30 inches may be adequate for arable cultivation, but when this average is in fact derived from extremes of 10 inches one year and 40 to 50 the next, the famine of the one year resulting from drought is matched by the famine of the next year resulting from excessive rainfall. Control of water supplies, whether for cultivation or for watering of stock, is priority No. 1 in all tropical lands.

That we have not yet reached the stage when we can safely apply our knowledge of land management gained from mid-latitudes to the conquest of tropical lands is well illustrated by the fate of the bold experiment in East Africa, well known, some would say notorious, as the Groundnut Scheme. Because of the world shortage of fats and available oils, the British government determined on the reclamation of some three-and-a-quarter million acres of almost uninhabited tropical savanna in East Africa for groundnut (peanut) production. The oil has a high nutrient quality, and since the plant is an annual, a quick return was expected. The goal was 600,-000 long tons of nuts a year. The original scheme, which was based on a report prepared by three experts, aimed at establishing 107 mechanized farm units of 30,000 acres each—80 in Tanganyika, 17 in Northern Rhodesia, and 10 in Kenya. In 1947, the first year, 150,000 acres were to be cleared and 450,000 acres in 1948.

The operation encountered innumerable difficulties. The first year saw only 30,000 acres planted, and the crop is said to have been less than the seed nuts put into the ground. Although it was claimed that the rains failed and that when they did come they caused great damage by flooding, washing away of railways and roads, etc., it is doubtful whether the seasons experienced actually were more unusual than usual. In an attempt to improve matters it was decided to change to a rotation of sunflowers, also for oil from the seeds, and cereals with the groundnuts.

In January, 1951, complete failure was admitted. The cost to that time was £36,000,000 of the British taxpayer's money or roughly $2 for every man, woman, and child in Britain. It was then decided to write off the whole of the colossal expenditure and to carry on with a few pilot experiments. So many things had gone wrong it is difficult to say which factors had contributed most. The scattered trees of the "bush" had learned to survive vagaries of rainfall by exceptionally long roots that defied the ordinary bulldozer. The soils presented extraordinary difficulties to mechanized equipment. Like most African soils they have been formed from the underlying rocks, and the quartz fragments derived from quartz veins are angular, not rounded. Set in a hard clay matrix they formed a rasp which ruined the disk plows. Under heavy machinery they consolidated like the angular fragments in a macadam road, making a surface no plant could break through.

Eventually man will tame and use such lands, but once more it is demonstrated that our present techniques are inadequate. We need to know how to manage tropical soils; we need effective control of water supply; we need to produce new plants, particularly nutritious grasses and strains of fodder crops such as the deep-rooted alfalfas and clovers developed in Queensland, so as to maintain a fodder supply throughout the year; and we need also much additional knowledge as to food crops that can be grown.

A short time ago the failure of another government-sponsored African development project was reported, the Gambia poultry-farming scheme. It is worth quoting from a London *Times* editorial on the subject: [8]

The forces of nature are strong in the tropics and the conversion of bush into productive farming land is more than a task for bulldozers. The soil and its defects have to be closely studied. Usually there are good reasons why the natives have left the bush to nature. The time for bold investment is when scientists and agriculturists can diagnose the deficiencies and advise with some assurance on how they can be met.

But the Gambia has also witnessed an example in the way of wisdom—thorough investigation.

EXPERIMENT IN THE GAMBIA

An exceptionally interesting series of experiments has been carried out in the Gambia by a party of medical and nutrition experts working in conjunction with agriculturalists. The area selected for study centered on a village about 150 miles up the river from the coast. Climatically Geneiri is on the drier margin of the tropical belt. It has been described as having no average rainfall and no average temperature.

Climatic data for this precise spot are not available, but conditions are somewhat more erratic than at Bathurst on the coast, where recorded rainfalls (inches) for the rainy season are:

	May	June	July	August	Sept.	Oct.	Nov.
Max.	1.90	12.32	13.93	19.56	13.08	9.08	0.20
Min.	0.00	2.24	5.10	6.79	5.78	0.24	0.00

In any given year deficiencies in one month may be made up in another—often, however, with a disastrous effect on crops—but even yearly totals show a range over an eighteen-year period from 23.68 inches to 56.07 with an average of 43.36. If we regard 40 inches as the "safety line," this is how the eighteen years, 1901–18, worked out:

1901						1910				1918	
45	57	66	64	44	57	44		49	48	54	
40											40
	29	38		34		28	34	24	38	38	

The sequence of three bad years is particularly note-worthy, especially when one remembers that evaporation in these latitudes is at least equivalent to twenty inches of rain.

Geneiri exists on subsistence agriculture, some eighty per cent of the villagers' diet consisting of cereals. Interestingly enough no less than four or even five cereals enter into the diet, chiefly because the harvest is thereby spread over some five or six months of the year from late July or mid-August, when maize is available, to January or early February, when the last of the rice is harvested. Maize is followed by sorghum, then by *Pennisetum* (bulrush millet) and finally by *Digitaria* (finger grass) and rice. The remainder of the diet is from leafy vegetables such as okra, occasional fish, and, on rare occasions, chicken, goat, or beef. The people are poor farmers. All work is by hand, and out of the 2,000-acre area proper to the village, perhaps a couple of hundred acres is cultivated, probably the limit of which they are physically capable.

As a result existence is essentially from hand to mouth. The food is eaten as produced. It has been rightly said that the human body is there submitted twice a year to opposite types of maltreatment: too much food for a short season with consequent digestive troubles, too little food in the dry season, the so-called "hungry season," with consequent recurrent famine edema. Malnutrition is apparent in the physical appearance and weight of the villagers. In July when they were well fed the average weight of the adults was 130 pounds; in the following dry season the average weight had dropped to 120 pounds, this just at a time when physical energy was needed to prepare the land for the new crop. With the introduction of new food supplies weight increased. The experimenters, by importing food, succeeded after two seasons (1947–49) in maintaining the average weight and indeed increasing it to 139 pounds over the period July, 1947 to April, 1949. It was found, however, as in the case of the good feeding of African troops, that the effects of malnutrition during early years could not be completely eliminated by diet in adolescents and adults. This last point is highly significant; it means that a generation or more must pass before the general level of health and stamina can be built up; it underlines the impossibility of rapid development in tropical lands.

On the agricultural side the group carried out three parallel experiments: the encouragement of native agriculture; experimental farming with modern machinery on selected blocks of land cleared for the purpose; and a partnership under an arrangement whereby the village shared the produce. In addition to encouraging the growth of cereals, the further cultivation of groundnuts as a cash crop was promoted. The Africans, working by hand, obtained a maximum production of 250 pounds of groundnuts per acre, with plants rather widely spaced. By introducing full-scale mechanical cultivation (a Fordson tractor and a Fergusson tractor being used with both disk plows and light steel plows, seed sown mechanically, etc.) it was found possible to treble the number of plants per acre to 50,000 and so to step up the production to a maximum of 900 pounds per acre.

At first sight this would seem to be satisfactory, but although the number of plants per acre was increased and hence the production speeded up, the yield per plant remained low and the plants appeared to be suffering from some deficiency disease not understood. Strip cropping was adopted to prevent soil erosion, but the formation of hardpan and the difficulties of proper drainage combined with aeration of the soil have not yet been overcome. Presuming the equipment to be supplied free of capital cost, the financial results of the experiment when carried out cooperatively with the natives showed at the end a profit of about one shilling per day per laborer, or less than fifteen cents. This is half the normal local wage of labor employed by the day in the area.

In the meantime, by establishment of medical services, general health conditions had been greatly improved. The villagers expressed their appreciation of their contacts with Western civilization by saying, "Before our babies die, now they live." And thus we come back once again to the crucial question of the increasing pressure on the land. The Gambia experiment shows how many are the difficulties still to be overcome in the development of tropical lands, even with all the skill and the implements available to us.

WATER CONTROL AND IRRIGATION IN THE TROPICS

If variability of rainfall from year to year is the greatest single difficulty in the development of tropical lands, it follows almost automatically that the control of water supplies is the first need in most of those lands. Where the rain is heavy, there must be control to help runoff without causing soil erosion and to prevent disastrous flooding, but to permit adequate flooding of rice fields. Where rainfall is moderate, water control is needed as insurance against bad seasons and still more to provide for the dry season—"the hungry season" of Africa—and thus to permit a wider range of crops and longer growing period and extended harvests. Where rainfall is scanty this becomes even more necessary; where rainfall is both small and unreliable, irrigation is vital to settlement and development.

That the Nile is the lifeblood of Egypt is well known. That British-Indian government irrigation schemes have added to the productive lands of India and Pakistan many times the area of Egypt is less often appreciated. At the present day the Uganda Hydro-Electric Commission's scheme to harness the head waters of the Nile and the Kariba Gorge scheme on the Zambezi between Northern and Southern Rhodesia are two examples from underdeveloped Africa of bold schemes that combine water control with power development.

Reviewing the problem in tropical Africa, Professor Frank Debenham [9] has urged that, ideally, no water at all should be allowed to escape to the oceans—it is all needed for agriculture. In contrast to the great hydro-electric and irrigation schemes that have been proposed, he considers that Africans could be taught to do much to help themselves. He advocates control of runoff and temporary storage of water by erecting earth dams across small valleys and piping supplies to villages for domestic needs and to fields for watering cattle; and the use of falling water for grinding mills to save much of the drudgery in the life of African women and release their energies for other purposes. Where circumstances are favorable—which is only locally the case in Africa— water is best stored underground, where both contamination and loss by evaporation are minimized and the water can be reached by wells. In contrast to the peoples of India and many other countries, the African is little accustomed to the use of wells. Such simple methods extend the availability of water supplies and cut down the "hungry" season, eliminate much of the wasted labor in fetching supplies and lower the prevalence of disease resulting from contaminated water.

In hot, dry lands, especially when swept by wind, water in the soil evaporates quickly, leaving behind contained salts. Irrigation schemes may be outstandingly successful for a few years, but then accumulation of alkaline salts in the surface layers of the soil begins to affect cultivation. Enough flowing water to wash salts out of the soil is needed—a delicate balance must be

maintained. Anyone who has flown over irrigated northern India will have noticed what appears from the air to
be an attack of measles or some skin disease of the land.
This is the first danger signal of increasing alkalinity,
and it is not so easily seen on the ground as from the
air. Dr. H. L. Hoskins, writing on "Point IV with Reference to the Middle East," [10] believes the abandonment of old irrigation settlements in Iran, Iraq, and
elsewhere in the Middle East to be due to alkalinity. He
quotes a modern case: "the famed Al Kharj oasis in
Saudi Arabia. Here in a two thousand acre tract is the
model farm of King ibn-Saud. Under the direction of
an American agricultural expert and staff and financed
by the King's oil royalties, experiments are undertaken
in the development of food and forage plants adapted
to the Arabian environment. From the horticultural
point of view the undertaking has been a distinct success, but in another respect it is probably doomed to
eventual failure. The tract is watered from a deep natural reservoir, whose waters are hardly potable. Every
irrigation channel is rimmed with alkaline salts. . . .
from year to year as new sections are put to the plow,
others must be abandoned as no longer productive."

MID-LATITUDE COMPARISONS

I have devoted considerable space to the consideration
of the equatorial and tropical climates because these
include the most important of the underdeveloped or
undeveloped lands of the world. When we turn for purposes of comparison to the middle latitudes, those famil-

iar to us in the United States or in Europe, we are reminded at once of the relative kindliness of nature in
providing climatic conditions more directly suited to
the production of man's principal food crops. We shall
examine later conditions in the British Isles, but in
passing we may repeat the statement that for many
farming purposes climatic conditions common to northwestern Europe are ideal. With average temperatures in
the coldest month above 32° F., it is never too cold for
outdoor farming operations; with an average temperature in the hottest month between 55° and 72° or
73° F., it is never too hot in the summer for outdoor occupations. The seasonal rhythm of summer and winter
is such as to produce a welcome resting period, but a
long period of vegetative growth. The climate certainly
is ideal for grass and other fodder crops. The precipitation, mainly as rain, coming in almost equal amounts in
each of the months throughout the year, keeps the land
green and fertile, and rarely is water supply a source of
real anxiety. In the drier parts of these lands summer
sunshine is adequate for ripening of grain.

Let us transfer the picture to the mid-latitude continental climate, that of the heart of the United States
and Canada, where colder winters provide a longer resting period, where frost helps the farmer's plow in breaking up the heavier soils and in destroying some of the
pests which might otherwise survive. The summers have
adequate warmth and sunshine to provide excellent
ripening conditions for cereal crops, conditions not far
from ideal from the point of view of the cereal farmer.

If we may jump ahead to an obvious conclusion which I shall endeavor later to substantiate, it is that there are greater immediate prospects of increasing agricultural output in the middle latitudes than there is of securing immediate help in the world food situation from much more difficult tropical lands. In other words, we shall be looking for the underdeveloped areas at least as much in our familiar middle latitudes as we shall be in the doubtful Eldorados of the tropics.

RURAL POPULATION DENSITIES

In the foregoing sections on tropical environment we have been considering essentially what possibilities exist, in the first place, of ameliorating conditions of life for the inhabitants who are mostly primary producers; in the second place, how the environmental factors can be so brought under control that the land can support more people; in the third place, how a surplus of primary produce can be secured for export to the hungry peoples of urbanized lands. In the urbanized industrial countries of middle latitudes there also are rural populations, but they present new or different problems. So we pass for a moment to an entirely different matter, the carrying capacity of agricultural lands in terms of human beings; in other words, the number of people per square mile that can be supported by different types of agricultural development. In my presidential address before Section E (Geography) of the 1949 meeting of the British Association for the Advancement of Science, I developed the concept that we can distinguish three groups of people in the rural category: (1) the primary rural population which consists of farmers and farm workers, together with their dependents, who derive their living directly from the land; (2) the secondary rural population which exists to serve the primary group and is necessary for the maintenance of the rural population structure, including storemen, shopkeepers, garage mechanics, and transport workers, who serve the farmers and farm workers, together with postal officials, doctors, veterinary surgeons, and others living in villages and small towns and essential to the life of the countryside; (3) the adventitious population which includes people who live in rural areas by choice rather than by necessity, commuters and retired townsfolk.

By some the last named, the retired people, have been regarded as mere parasites. Closer consideration shows what an important part they frequently play because they have greater leisure for carrying out those innumerable voluntary tasks inevitably associated with local government, whether of an incorporated village or an English parish. We shall deal at a later stage with some aspects of this rural population question. In many parts of the world great benefits accrue to the life of the remoter country areas from the visitors who occupy summer cottages or summer homes and who restore and reoccupy old farmsteads and cottages.

We are familiar with the universal phenomenon of rural depopulation, the drift to the towns, which is so often regarded as synonymous with decay of rural life and with a decreasing importance of agriculture. But, in fact, an opposite cause may be operating: in any given type of farming an increase in productive efficiency, such as the extension of mechanization, lowers the labor requirements and so leads to rural depopulation, even in those areas where farming is prosperous and increasingly efficient. This is certainly the position in many of the countries of the Old World.

CARRYING CAPACITY OF THE WORLD'S LANDS

For reasons outlined in the preceding section we must accept with the utmost caution estimates of the carrying capacity associated with different types of land use. We have already spoken of the extremely high densities of rural population in parts of China and India. It has been estimated that an ordinary rice economy can comfortably support more than 700 persons to the square mile in Java. In the mid-latitudes, for example in Europe, where peasant agriculture is still the general rule, surprisingly high rural densities are possible, though at this stage we raise no question of their standard of living. The calculations which I have recently made in England show the carrying capacity of the typical moderate-class farmland of the heart of England to be of the order of fifty to sixty persons per square mile of the primary rural population,[11] to which one adds fifty per cent to cover the secondary rural population. There are many who would point out that production as efficient as that in the Midlands of England could be obtained by a smaller population, and that is a question which I propose to examine later.

It is clear, however, that we are faced with two entirely different questions. The first is the maximum number of people which a square mile of productive land can support in terms of food. The second is the population needed to secure maximum production with maximum efficiency. The first may be of the order of 640—one person an acre—but the second will be hotly disputed according to views as to what constitutes efficiency in agriculture.

CHAPTER IV

Food for All

Food for all is the crucial problem of the world today for several reasons. A hungry world is never likely to be a peaceful world. It is not saying too much to suggest that unrest throughout the world most frequently has its root cause in dissatisfaction with that part of the standard of living concerned with food. As Le Gros Clark has put it, a stable civilization will be built only on the foundations of the farm and the kitchen.

We do well to remind ourselves that we consume food for three reasons. A large part of the food we eat keeps us going and provides the body with its heat and energy. It has precisely the same function as fuel performs with our modern machinery. However perfect the machine, it will not function without the right fuel in adequate quantities. Vaguely this idea has been apparent to man for a long time. Our ancestors used to talk about a man's strength failing through lack of food. If for a short time the intake of this fuel is inadequate, the body is able to call upon reserves normally stored in the tissues, but ultimately this stored material is used up and starvation results. For the fuel purpose of food we are concerned particularly with carbohydrates—our daily bread.

In the second place, we consume food for building up the machine itself, that is to say for the development of the body. It is for this purpose that we require particularly the complex substances known as proteins, builders of muscles and other tissues. We have come to realize in recent years the important part played also by those essential substances to which the term vitamin is applied. They are diverse in chemical composition and in function, and they are only required in small quantities; yet they are fundamental in the body's economy, and the body itself cannot manufacture them from simple raw materials. In rather the same way certain chemical elements are necessary in small quantities—calcium for bone, minute quantities of iodine for teeth, small quantities of iron for healthy red blood, and so on.

Thirdly, we consume food for what perhaps might be called its psychological effect. In these days the art of gracious living, to which our ancestors were perhaps too much addicted, has been almost forgotten, but probably all of us appreciate that a tastefully served and well-balanced meal, eaten in pleasant surroundings, gives us a greater satisfaction than the same mixture of carbohydrates, proteins, and vitamins consumed from a tin mug on the floor. A graphic illustration is afforded by a recent experiment carried out in a British hospital. Groups of people were served with first-class food—good meat and well-cooked potatoes, but the meat was colored green and the potatoes magenta and other fierce colors. The majority of the "guinea pigs" were so affected psychologically that they were ill after eating the completely innocuous meal.

In the long view a monotonous diet, even if pronounced adequate, will not necessarily maintain the full vigor of either individual or nation, however satisfactory it may be during stress, as in war time. The widely held view that many people live on an extremely monotonous diet and like it—one thinks of the boiled rice, occasionally flavored with a little fat pork, and the weak tea of the Chinese—is far from the truth. Given the opportunity and the means, all peoples turn to a varied diet. I have often thought that the finest advice on the subject was that given by the English musical-comedy actress Marie Lloyd in her song of long ago, "A Little of What You Fancy Does You Good!"

With these preliminaries in mind we may refer first to the question of daily caloric intake. The caloric intake is a measure of the adequacy of the fuel supply. Where it is more than 3,000 units a day, it is adequate for all purposes and it may even be excessive. Where it drops below 2,000 it is below the danger line. Dr. H. R. Tolley of FAO has stated that the minimum desirable caloric intake is between 2,550 and 2,650 a day.[1] In the United States the caloric intake averaged 3,240 in 1935–39, and it was the same in 1948. It ranged from a low of 3,160 in 1935 to a high of 3,490 in 1928 over a thirty-year period. These figures are obtained by dividing total calorie-consumption by total population. In view of the very large proportion of food wasted during and after cooking, the actual caloric intake is doubtless much less than these figures suggest (see below p. 91). It should be noted that when we measure the output of land in terms of calories we measure in essence the output of human fuel.

An adequate fuel intake, however, is not enough; other essentials enter in. Though there may not be hunger as such, a nutritional problem may exist all the same. The nutritional approach to the problem of feeding human beings in large numbers came to the forefront in World War II. In Britain a Ministry of Food was established as a wartime measure. The Ministry's experts worked out an acceptable diet from nutritional standards and sought to provide it by home production expanded and modified, together with the necessary minimum import. The British farmer was required to concentrate on cereals and potatoes to supply the carbohydrates needed in the supply of human fuel, though with the lowering of the consumption of meat and of the number of animals kept and slaughtered in the country for that purpose the individual's protein intake was reduced. There is no doubt that the whole was well and scientifically worked out and the amazingly good health record of the country during the war is evidence of its success. It is interesting to recall how the third aspect, the palatability of food, caused a minor crisis in the early days of the war. Dietitians will agree that there is little nutritive value in a fried onion compared with other food available, but not only are fried onions able to permeate a home with an odor delectable to some, if

odious to others; they also give an almost romantic aroma
to the tasteless mixture of bread flavored with meat
scraps put into a skin and called a sausage. And the
British, to give zest to their dull, if adequate, wartime
diet, demanded onions!

There are many who urge that more attention be
given to the protein intake and that in any case carbohydrates derived from such high protein foods as
butcher's meat have a greater effectiveness in their task
of maintaining human energy. Despite the health record
of Britain and other European countries, there does
seem to be some evidence of loss of reserve of stamina or
reserve of strength traceable to the lower protein intake.

ESTIMATES OF WORLD FOOD PRODUCTION

If it is difficult to estimate world population, it is even
more difficult to estimate the world's food production.
As a preliminary, we may look at Table VI, which gives
some world figures. We note first that the area of cereals
harvested averages about half an acre per capita of the
world's population, and yields about twelve bushels per
capita. Rather more than a quarter is rice, rather less
than a quarter wheat. We may presume that most of the
rice and wheat is for direct human consumption, and so
is most of the rye, but only small proportions of the barley, oats, and corn (maize). Thus the world's 2,350,000,-
000 people eat 384,900,000,000 pounds of wheat; 10,-
200,000,000 pounds of rye; and 411,000,000,000 pounds
of rice—let us say 900,000,000,000 pounds of cereals a
year, or a little more than one pound per capita a day.

TABLE VI. SUMMARY OF WORLD PRODUCTION OF CEREAL CROPS*

	Areas harvested Thousands of acres			Production Millions of bushels		
	1935–39	1946	1948	1935–39	1946	1948
Wheat	418,090	386,280	415,500	6,010	5,704	6,415
Rye	100,900	102,100	109,070	1,731	1,380	1,670
Barley	116,050	106,850	113,770	2,363	2,082	2,395
Oats	143,750	131,280	129,790	4,364	3,920	4,230
Corn	220,820	210,680	210,380	4,750	5,276	5,975
Rice	206,500	207,000	215,300	7,455	6,929	7,473
	1,206,110	1,144,190	1,193,810	26,673	25,291	28,158

* From *The Statesman's Year Book, 1949*.

With a smaller world acreage harvested, the excess of production in 1948 over the prewar average is almost entirely due to increased yields of corn (maize) and wheat in the United States.

One kilogram (2⅕ lbs.) of wheat flour represents 3,640 calories, one kilogram of rice 3,540, so that one pound of cereal may be regarded as roughly representing 1,650 calories.

The most serious omission from the above table is of the various small grains, collectively known as millets, which are widely used in the drier parts of tropical lands especially Africa and Asia.

This works out to some 1,650 calories a day, almost exactly half the figure for the United States. If we accept 2,500 calories a day as a proper standard for health, we see how this figure reflects a low standard for the world as a whole.

Of course, these rough calculations leave many facts out of consideration. Cereals are by no means the only source of calories, though for 97 per cent of mankind they are the chief source and for nearly two-thirds of mankind they, with potatoes, provide more than 80 per cent of the total caloric intake. Table VI does not include millets, peas, beans, potatoes, and other energy-giving starchy foods, but this is compensated for by the

inclusion of all wheat and rice, regardless of the amounts
fed to animals or devoted to industrial uses.

The crude method of obtaining caloric intake from
total food consumption divided by the number of people ignores both different age compositions and food
wastage. Where the proportion wasted is exceptionally
high, as in the United States, the net caloric intake is
obviously lower. Whereas the gross figure quoted above
for the United States is 3,240 calories a day, the net is
probably well below 3,000. Indeed, J. D. Black and
M. E. Kiefer consider it to be 2,540—the rest is wasted.[2]

It would be wrong to suggest that caloric intake is a
complete guide to living standards. The body has more
work to do in maintaining bodily heat in cold climates
than in hot, as it has in winter compared with summer.
Body weight is another factor. Taking two individuals
both engaged in heavy manual work, a Canadian lum-
berjack weighing 200 pounds working in winter requires a far larger caloric intake than an Indian dock
worker weighing 130 pounds working in the humid
heat of Bombay. If climate and body weight are taken
into consideration there is found to be a smaller difference between one country and another than the crude
figures would suggest.

The oft-repeated statement that world food supply is
failing to keep pace with world population is usually
based essentially on the production of staple foods, the
cereals and potatoes. But it is the world-wide rule that,
as standards of living rise, there is less and less dependence on these staples and more on a varied diet. In the

years before the outbreak of World War II it was estimated that the peoples of the United States, Canada,
New Zealand, Australia, Britain, Switzerland, and Sweden—11 per cent of mankind, with the highest food
standards—derived less than 40 per cent of their caloric
intake from the staples. Most of the countries of western
Europe derived less than 50 per cent from cereals.[3]

As M. K. Bennett, Executive Director of the Food
Research Institute of Stanford University, has emphasized on several occasions, a decreasing per capita consumption of cereals may indicate an increasing standard
of living. The statement applies to most, if not to all,
of the nations belonging to the commercial Western
world. Dr. Bennett postulates that a race of millionaires
would not rely on cereals for more than 10 to 20 per
cent of caloric intake.[4]

Elsewhere we urge that extensive farming, with huge
areas devoted to one crop such as wheat or corn and
emphasis on low cost per unit produced, is an obsoles-
cent type of land use and, for the conservation of the
land itself, must give place to a balanced type of mixed
farming, probably in small units. This seems also to be
the lesson to be drawn from studies of changes in human tastes and the trend towards a varied diet.

COMPARISONS AND CONTRASTS BETWEEN COUNTRIES

Since one of our main objects is to discover which of
the countries of the world may justifiably be described
as underdeveloped, we need to examine existing production in individual countries. A country may be un-

derdeveloped either because it has land which could
be, but is not, actually productive or because existing
production from its farmed lands is below standard, as
evidenced by the yield of crops per unit area.

Table VII shows yield for each of the main cereals
and for sugar, cane and beet. It is taken from FAO's
Yearbook of Food and Agricultural Statistics.[5] The
values of quintals and hectares have been converted to
bushels an acre. For each crop the countries are ar-
ranged in order of yield per unit area—above and below the world average—for the prewar quinquennium
1934–38. For comparison, calculated yields for the years
1945–47 are shown.

In 1934–38 the leading places for each of the mid-
latitude cereals and sugar beet are taken by the intensively farmed countries of northwestern Europe—Denmark, Netherlands, Belgium, Britain, and Germany.
The "new countries" with extensive farming methods—
the United States, Canada, Argentina, and Australia—
are well down on the list and are in most cases well
below world average. Parenthetically it should be noted
that in choosing a quinquennium it is difficult to avoid
years of bad harvest, unfair to some countries. The year
1934, for example, was a disastrous one in parts of the
United States, and 1936 was also bad in some areas. The
year 1946 was bad in many parts of Europe.

The effect of the war is evident in nearly all European countries in lowered yields, though the disastrous
situation in 1945 is partly offset by later recovery. In
contrast a remarkable improvement in yields is seen

TABLE VII. CROP YIELD BY COUNTRIES
Bushels per acre

WHEAT (1 bushel = 60 lbs.)

	1934–38	1945–47
Denmark	45.5	43.8
Netherlands	45.4	30.3
Belgium	40.9	30.2
Great Britain	34.6	32.5
Germany	34.5	—
Egypt	30.1	18.6
Japan	28.2	18.0
France	23.4	18.6
Italy	21.6	16.5
Europe Average	21.1	16.0
Hungary	21.0	13.8
China	16.2	16.2
WORLD AVERAGE	15.1	14.8
Argentina	15.7	16.9
Spain	15.4	10.9
(U.S.S.R.)	13.9	—
United States	13.0	17.7
Pakistan	12.7	12.3
Australia	12.0	12.6
Canada	10.6	—
India	10.3	8.8

RICE (Paddy) (1 bushel = 45 lbs.)

	1934–38	1945–47
Spain	70.1	47.5
Italy	59.4	46.9
Australia	53.7	51.3
Japan	40.8	37.7
Egypt	39.2	39.3
China	28.4	28.4
British Guiana	27.9	28.0
United States	27.8	26.2
Korea	26.5	24.9
WORLD AVERAGE	19.7	18.5
Java	17.1	15.2
Pakistan	16.6	15.6
Brazil	16.1	17.8
Siam	16.1	14.0
Burma	15.9	14.1
India	14.7	13.5
Madagascar	13.8	14.1
Indo-China	13.0	12.5
Philippines	12.3	12.4

CORN (Maize) (1 bushel = 60 lbs.)

	1934–38	1945–47
Germany	42.6	25.6
Austria	38.2	20.8
(Canada)	37.9	
Egypt	37.3	30.9
Italy	30.7	20.8
Hungary	29.8	20.2
Argentina	27.1	30.1
France	23.7	11.7
Manchuria	22.6	19.8
United States	22.6	31.0
Europe Average	22.2	14.5
Brazil	20.8	19.8
China	20.7	20.2
WORLD AVERAGE	20.1	21.6
Bulgaria	16.9	9.6
Pakistan	16.6	15.9
(U.S.S.R.)	16.0	—
Rumania	15.6	10.9
Java	14.5	9.4
Africa Average	12.1	10.2
India	11.1	9.6
South Africa	? 9.0	?
Mexico	8.4	10.2

BARLEY (1 bushel = 56 lbs.)

	1934–38	1945–47
Denmark	41.7	43.4
Netherlands	41.7	34.6
Belgium	36.8	30.5
Eire	34.7	27.3
Germany	29.7	20.7
Great Britain	29.3	30.8
Japan	28.6	18.3
Norway	28.1	29.4
Egypt	27.7	24.1
Czechoslovakia	23.8	17.9
Poland	22.0	14.7
Europe Average	21.4	17.9
France	20.3	16.7
Hungary	18.5	12.6
Bulgaria	18.2	10.6
Spain	17.6	12.7
Iran	17.4	20.4
China	16.4	15.8
United States	16.2	19.0
WORLD AVERAGE	16.1	15.0
Turkey	15.4	11.1
Italy	15.4	10.5
Korea	15.1	10.9
Canada	14.7	16.1
(U.S.S.R.)	13.4	—
Peru	13.3	13.2
Australia	13.3	13.4
Argentina	13.2	16.9
India	11.8	11.9
Pakistan	10.9	10.2
Rumania	9.9	5.9
Morocco	9.4	8.1
Algeria	8.0	5.6

TABLE VII. CROP YIELD BY COUNTRIES—*Continued*

Bushels per acre

OATS (1 bushel = 40 lbs.)	1934–38	1945–47	RYE (1 bushel = 60 lbs.)	1934–38	1945–47
Denmark	26.8	28.8	Belgium	35.8	26.5
Belgium	26.8	23.3	Netherlands	34.0	23.5
Netherlands	25.5	20.5	Sweden	28.9	23.5
Eire	24.5	20.8	Germany	26.8	20.7
Germany	20.6	15.0	Denmark	26.7	25.9
Great Britain	20.4	20.4	Czechoslovakia	24.0	20.2
New Zealand	19.7	21.7	Australia	22.0	—
Sweden	18.9	13.8			
Czechoslovakia	16.2	12.6	*Europe Average*	21.3	15.0
Europe Average	15.7	13.1	Italy	20.1	14.4
Poland	14.5	8.9			
Japan	14.1	8.0	WORLD AVERAGE	19.6	14.5
France	13.9	12.1			
WORLD AVERAGE	11.9	11.9	Poland	19.2	12.0
			France	17.4	13.0
Chile	10.1	8.8	Hungary	16.6	12.7
(U.S.S.R.)	10.0	—	(U.S.S.R.)	14.8	—
United States	9.9	12.3	Spain	13.9	9.7
Turkey	9.8	6.8	United States	11.5	11.8
Argentina	9.4	10.4	Canada	9.1	11.2
Canada	9.2	10.5	Argentina	8.7	9.3
Spain	8.6	7.6			
China	8.5	7.4			
Rumania	7.8	4.3			
Australia	4.9	6.1			

Tons per acre

SUGAR CANE			SUGAR BEETS		
Hawaii	60.4	?	Netherlands	15.2	12.5
Java (plantations)	52.0	?	Sweden	14.5	12.9
Peru	40.9	44.8	Denmark	14.4	13.2
Egypt	32.7	27.0	Germany	12.1	8.6
Jamaica	25.3	?	Belgium	11.6	10.3
Puerto Rico	23.9	?	Czechoslovakia	11.4	7.8
Fiji	21.6	?	France	11.0	9.2
Australia	20.7	19.0			
Mexico	18.6	21.0	*Europe Average*	11.0	8.2
United States	17.3	17.7			
Mauritius	16.8	17.5	WORLD AVERAGE	10.6	8.6
Trinidad	16.4	14.5			
Cuba	15.1	15.5	Poland	10.5	?
Brazil	15.0	14.6	United States	10.0	11.8
			Italy	10.0	7.6
WORLD AVERAGE	14.3	13.8	Canada	8.9	9.5
			Great Britain	8.8	9.0
Philippines	14.0	?	(U.S.S.R.)	5.6	—
Argentina	12.8	13.5			
South Africa	10.3	?			
India	?	?			

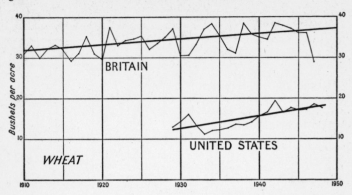

Fig. 22. Wheat yields in Britain and the United States.

in most of the newer countries, especially in the United
States, which has shot up to above world average (except
in rye), though it remains far below the northwestern
European countries. The phenomenal results of hybrid-
corn yields are at once outstanding: the increase in the
world total and world average is almost entirely due
to the huge increase in the United States, the world's
largest producer. Some marked improvements in yield
are also seen in other big producers, notably Canada
and Argentina, but Australia continues to suffer from
rainfall variability as well as from the wartime deple-
tion of manpower. The tragically low place occupied by
India and Pakistan we shall consider later (Chap. VI).

What are the chief lessons to be learned from this
table? In the first place is the high yield associated with
the intensive farming systems of northwestern Europe
and the resulting difficulty of increasing yield and output.

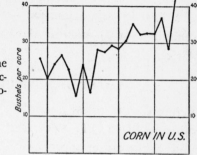

Fig. 23. Corn yields in the United States. The spectacular rise follows the introduction of hybrid corn.

In the second place is the progress being made in the "newer" countries of mid-latitudes and the enormous possibilities of increased yield and hence total production before the highest European standards are reached.

In the third place is the continuing struggle against

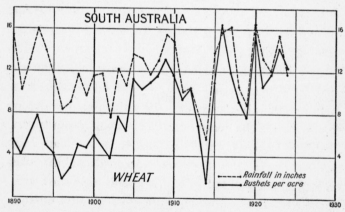

Fig. 24. Wheat yields in South Australia (after A. Grenfell Price). Yields are closely dependent on the rainfall of the winter and spring preceding the harvest.

nature shown in the low yields of tropical countries and those in the warmer parts of mid-latitudes with unreliable rainfall—notably Australia, Spain, and North Africa.

MEASUREMENT OF AGRICULTURAL EFFICIENCY

Before we can assess underdevelopment, we need some measure of the efficiency of existing production. We must at the outset appreciate the fact, not by any means fully recognized, that there are at least two entirely different approaches to the subject. The one approach regards efficiency as indicated by output per unit area, the other measures efficiency in terms of the output of labor, that is per man-hour. The issue is further complicated when the value of output is introduced, especially with the absurdities that result if values are expressed according to the present arbitrary rates of exchange between the world's currencies. A nearer approximation is reached when values are measured in terms of real wages.

In a world short of food it is surely clear that what matters is the actual amount of food produced, so, making some allowance for quality, the higher the output per unit area the greater the efficiency of the farmer. In Table VII the central datum line is the calculated average world yield for the crop concerned. Taking wheat as typical for mid-latitude cereals and using the average for the interwar quinquennium 1934–38, we find at the top of the list Denmark, Holland, Belgium, and Britain which, on this showing, are the most efficient producers in the world. A long way down the list, on this basis to be regarded as inefficient producers, are Canada, the United States, Argentina, and Australia. However, to base our judgment on one crop only is to fall into error; and there is the difficulty of comparing efficiencies, say between wheat and rice producers.

An attempt to meet the difficulty of measuring agricultural productivity is shown in Figure 25, which deals with Europe only. Huntington and Van Valkenburg used the eight widely raised crops, wheat, rye, barley, oats, corn, potatoes, sugar beet, and hay; for each crop the yield per acre for Europe as a whole was called 100 and the yield in each country calculated accordingly. The outstanding fact is that the countries of northwestern Europe, headed by Belgium, Holland, Denmark, and England, reached the highest level of more than 150 per cent. Conversely, in the countries of Mediterranean and eastern Europe the intensity of agriculture drops below 100, the lowest recorded being 57 per cent in Greece.

The subject has been approached as a mathematical problem by Professor M. G. Kendall, of the London School of Economics.[6] Taking the acre yields of ten leading crops in each of the forty-eight administrative counties in England for four selected years, he tried out four coefficients—productivity, ranking, money value, and starch equivalent or energy. So far as I know, his method has never been worked out on an international basis, and here I propose to make the attempt. His first coefficient involves mathematics beyond the

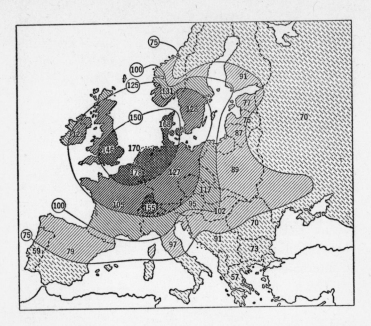

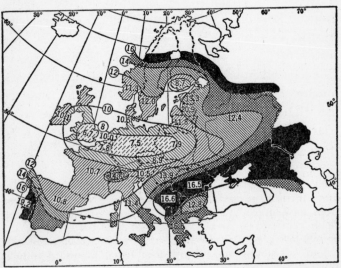

Figs. 25-26. *(Caption on facing page.)*

power of the nonexpert and the use of a calculating machine. As Kendall himself said, "The labor required prompted me to look for a coefficient which, though perhaps of doubtful theoretical meaning, might lead to similar results in practice." He accordingly devised his "ranking coefficient."

The purpose of the "ranking coefficient" is to put in order any given number of countries growing the same range of crops. Kendall's attempt to rank the English counties was vitiated by the fact that he had to ignore pasture land, so very important in English farming. However, this consideration should not seriously affect an international comparison.

For my purpose I have selected twenty countries— the United States, Canada, Argentina, Chile, Australia, New Zealand, Japan, China, India, Egypt, Italy, Spain, France, Belgium, Netherlands, Denmark, Germany, Austria, Eire, and Britain; and nine crops—wheat, rye, barley, oats, corn, potatoes, sugar beet, beans, and peas. The selected crops are grown in nearly all the countries, but for some, averages for certain crops only could be used. The method is simple. For each crop the countries are placed in order of output per acre, that is, from 1 to 20 (Table VIII). The place occupied by each

Figs. 25-26 *(opposite)*. Agriculture in Europe. Fig. 25 *(top)* shows intensity of agriculture; 100 is the yield per acre for eight crops for Europe as a whole. Fig. 26 shows variability of crop yields expressed as average percentage of departure from the normal for 1927–33. (Reproduced by permission from *Europe* by S. Van Valkenburg and Ellsworth Huntington, published by John Wiley & Sons, Inc., 1935.)

TABLE VIII. COMPARISON OF TWENTY SELECTED COUNTRIES IN ACRE-YIELDS OF NINE CROPS

Countries numbered in order of yield per acre for each crop

1934–38	Wheat	Rye	Barley	Oats	Corn	Potatoes	Sugar beets	Beans	Peas	Average
Austria	10	8	10	8	4	7	6	4	8	7.2
Belgium	3	1	3	1	3	1	4	—	2	2.2
Denmark	1	6	1	1	—	4	2	—	3	2.6
France	11	6	12	10	10	11	5	11	7	9.2
Germany	5	4	5	5	2	6	3	3	6	4.3
Ireland	6	3	4	4	—	2	9	—	—	4.7
Italy	12	9	16	11	7	18	8	13	14	12.0
Netherlands	2	2	1	3	12	3	1	1	1	2.9
Spain	16	10	13	17	9	10	10	12	16	12.6
U. K.	4	5	6	6	—	5	2	—	—	4.7
Canada	19	14	17	15	5	14	11	5	11	12.3
U. S. A.	17	11	15	13	11	16	7	7	9	12.0
Argentina	15	15	19	14	8	20	15	10	13	14.3
Chile	14	13	11	12	15	15	—	9	14	12.9
China	13	—	14	16	15	19	14	6	12	13.6
India	20	—	20	—	17	13	—	—	17	17.8
Japan	9	—	8	9	14	12	13	8	10	10.4
Egypt	8	—	9	—	6	9	—	2	4	6.3
Australia	18	12	18	18	13	17	—	—	—	16.0
N. Z.	7	—	7	7	1	8	—	—	5	5.8

1946	Wheat	Rye	Barley	Oats	Corn	Potatoes	Sugar beets	Beans	Peas	Average
Austria	13	8	17	12	8	13	12	7	11	11.2
Belgium	3	1	3	2	2	3	3	3	1	2.3
Denmark	1	5	1	1	—	5	2	—	2	2.4
France	9	7	10	7	16	10	5	13	4	9.0
Germany	8	6	9	8	9	7	9	4	8	7.6
Ireland	6	3	6	5	—	2	10	—	—	5.3
Italy	10	8	18	11	10	19	8	14	16	12.7
Netherlands	2	2	2	3	6	1	1	2	3	2.4
Spain	18	14	12	17	12	17	11	12	15	14.2
U. K.	5	4	4	6	—	4	6	—	—	4.8
Canada	13	10	13	10	3	12	7	5	9	9.1
U. S. A.	12	11	11	9	4	9	4	8	6	8.2
Argentina	16	13	14	13	5	20	—	6	12	12.4
Chile	11	12	8	14	11	11	—	11	14	11.5
China	15	—	15	15	4	18	—	9	13	12.7
India	19	—	19	—	17	13	—	—	17	17.0
Japan	17	—	16	16	15	15	—	10	10	14.1
Egypt	7	—	7	—	7	8	—	1	7	6.2
Australia	19	—	20	18	13	16	—	—	—	17.2
N. Z.	4	—	5	4	1	6	—	—	5	4.2

country is then averaged. If one country were at the top of every list it would have a ranking coefficient of one; if a country were at the bottom of every list (presuming each country to grow all the nine crops) it would have a ranking coefficient of twenty. Table IX is the result.

TABLE IX. TWENTY SELECTED COUNTRIES IN ORDER
OF FARMING EFFICIENCY (KENDALL'S
RANKING COEFFICIENT) *

1934–38		1946	
Belgium	2.2	Belgium	2.3
Denmark	2.6	Denmark	2.4
Netherlands	2.9	Netherlands	2.4
Germany	4.3	New Zealand	4.2
Britain	4.7	Britain	4.8
Ireland	4.7	Ireland	5.3
New Zealand	5.8	Egypt	6.2
Egypt	6.3	Germany	7.6
Austria	7.2	United States	8.2
France	9.2	France	9.0
Japan	10.4	Canada	9.1
Italy	12.0	Austria	11.2
United States	12.0	Chile	11.5
Canada	12.3	Argentina	12.4
Spain	12.6	China	12.7
Chile	12.9	Italy	12.7
China	13.6	Japan	14.1
Argentina	14.3	Spain	14.2
Australia	16.0	India	17.0
India	17.8	Australia	17.2

* See Table VIII for data from which constructed.

What, we may ask, does Kendall's ranking coefficient actually measure? The answer is simply that it measures crop productivity per unit area, which is the result partly of natural advantages of soil and climate, partly of farming efficiency. Kendall also determined money-value and starch-equivalent coefficients for corroborative purposes.

It should be noticed that starch equivalent or the commonly used caloric output per unit area [7] gives a measure of what has been described above as the output of food regarded as "human fuel."

Table IX at once confirms the consistently high level of farming efficiency in northwestern Europe. It also shows the high place occupied by New Zealand, which enjoys a similar type of reliable climate. The Mediterranean countries of Europe—Spain, Italy, and (in part) France—suffer from a less reliable rainfall, and it is primarily to this cause that we must attribute the low place occupied by Australia. The ravages of war explain the drop in the relative positions of Germany, Austria, and Japan. Wartime needs have given stimulus to the United States and Canada,[8] but they are still low in the table. Egypt illustrates how efficient a peasant agriculture can be in terms of output per unit area, whereas the position of India at the bottom of the table shows how advantages of climate can be offset by inefficient farming methods.

What, may we ask, is wrong—and it would seem obviously wrong—with this approach? It is, of course, the presumption that what matters is the amount of the output and that the labor involved is immaterial. We do well to look at the position in China. As emphasized long ago by King in his classic *Farmers of Forty Centuries,* nowhere in the world does agriculture reach the same levels of intensive production as in the more favored parts of China. Nature provides the essential elements of good, deep alluvial soils, adequate water supply, high summer temperatures, and a rhythm of seasons permitting a succession of crops on the same piece of land. Farming is of the intensive type that we associate with Chinese settlers elsewhere in the world, a type usually designated as "market gardening," or "truck farming." The saving of every scrap of organic matter, and particularly the composting for use as manure of human excreta and wastes, is an essential part of the system. What strikes the observer, of course, is the unceasing toil, the never-ending slavery of the work involved.

We may go to many other parts of the world and find examples of peasant subsistence agriculture where output per unit area reaches high levels. Perhaps of more significance is the obtaining of considerable outputs from land which could not be cultivated by other means. We can quote such diverse examples as the elaborate and laborious terracing of hillsides in tropical America, the peasant farms of the arid tracts of Portugal, or the little hill fields of remote parts of India. Are we justified in regarding production which involves such a staggering expenditure of direct human labor as efficient? Even in such areas as the southwest of England where the small "family farm" is the general rule, it can be shown [9] that, making allowance for even a nominal wage to the farmer's wife, the farmer, bearing all the responsibility and the burden of possible failure, is worse off financially than his hired man. Yet this type of farming persists and there is a waiting queue if a farm falls vacant. It has often been pointed out that

TABLE X. PERCENTAGE OF EMPLOYED POPULATION
ENGAGED IN AGRICULTURE*

Europe	Year	%	North America	Year	%
Austria	1934	31	Jamaica	1943	44
Belgium	1930	17	Canada	1941	30
Bulgaria	1934	80	Cuba	1943	41
Czechoslovakia	1930	37	Dominica	1935	77
Denmark	1930	34	El Salvador	1930	75
Finland	1930	64	Guatemala	1940	71
France	1936	36	Mexico	1930	67
Germany	1939	25	Nicaragua	1940	73
Greece	1946	58	Panama	1940	52
Hungary	1930	49	Puerto Rico	1940	45
Ireland	1936	49	United States	1940	20
Italy	1931	46			
Netherlands	1930	20			
Norway	1930	29	South America		
Poland	1931	64			
Portugal	1940	49	Brazil	1940	67
Rumania	1930	78	Chile	1930	36
Spain	1940	51	Colombia	1938	74
Sweden	1940	25	Peru	1940	62
Switzerland	1930	21	Venezuela	1941	50
United Kingdom	1939	5			
Yugoslavia	1931	78			
			Africa		
			Egypt	1937	70
Asia			Morocco	1936	74
Burma	1931	68	Nigeria	1931	74
Cyprus	1931	51	South Africa	1936	64
India	1931	66			
Indonesia	1930	66			
Japan	1940	43			
Malaya	1931	59			
Philippines	1939	65	Oceania		
Siam	1937	88	Australia	1933	23
Turkey	1935	82	New Zealand	1936	23

* Data from FAO.

two-thirds of the world's population is engaged in food production, and for the most part the food produced is inadequate even for the needs of the producer.

Can we therefore accept high output per unit area as an essential index of agricultural efficiency? Is it not obvious that the present world output could be maintained with the use of a very much smaller labor force? Such a viewpoint is natural in a country like the United States where land is abundant, labor scarce and expensive. But economy in manpower would not solve the problem in the closely settled countries of the Old World. In India and China it is land that is scarce, labor is abundant. The immediate result of "increasing efficiency" in the use of labor would be to create an unemployment problem, to drive the idle to the towns, and, it may be argued, to encourage the further development of an output of manufactured goods in excess of world requirements. Efficiency which results in shorter working hours and increase of available leisure is of course a separate matter.

If we turn now to the concept of efficiency as measured in terms of output per man-hour, then clearly every extension of mechanization is likely to lead to increased efficiency. The interesting example is, of course, what happened in Britain during the production campaign of World War II (Tables XI and XII). During that time Britain became the most highly mechanized farming country in the world. Broadly speaking every farmer possesses at least a tractor, and the horse has been completely eliminated on a very large number of farms. To the Fordson tractor, or an equivalent type, the farmers have gradually been adding a whole range of agricultural implements. Possibly the stage has already been reached when this procedure becomes inefficient, as when some machine is used only a few days of

TABLE XI. MECHANIZATION OF FARMING IN BRITAIN

	May, 1942	Jan., 1948
Tractors:		
Total	116,830	261,180
Tracklayers	5,600	15,200
3- and 4-wheeled	104,780	220,350
2-wheeled market-garden type	6,450	25,630
Moldboard plows:		
Total	465,630	462,940
Horsedrawn	353,180	218,380
Tractor drawn	112,450	244,560
Disk-harrows	33,840	76,060
Cultivators	161,690	256,670
Toolbars	14,340	46,550
Corndrills	101,550	119,730
Mowing machines	220,420	231,520
Binders	131,600	149,030
Threshing machines	13,150	15,860
Combine harvesters	1,000	5,220
Potato spinners	37,030	66,570
Milking machines	29,510	58,210
Work horses	585,000	457,000

The total number of "holdings"—many "part-time" or "hobby-farms" with some as small as one acre—is about 363,000 in England and Wales and 74,000 in Scotland, a total of about 437,000.

The total number of *full-time* farms or farmers in England and Wales is about 216,000 (1941 Farm Survey) to which should be added about 50,000 for Scotland, say 266,000 in all.

each year. Coupled with the facts expressed in Table XI are the reduction in working hours and the increase in wages, actual and real.

With extremely high acre-yields and high degree of mechanization, can we claim that Britain is the most efficiently farmed country in the world? If we take simply the criterion of output per man-hour, then Canada or large parts of the United States or, indeed, Australia or Argentina, with their reliance on large-scale machin-

TABLE XII. INCREASE IN FARMING EFFICIENCY IN GREAT BRITAIN

Per 100 acres of improved land (crops and grass)

	Workers	Arable %	Wheat acres	Total cattle	Milch cows	Sheep	Work horses
1874	4.7	58	11.6	19.6	—	97	4.2
1939	2.2	40	5.6	28.0	9.0	85	2.6
1945	2.9 [a]	61	11.2 [b]	31.0	9.4	65	—
1947 [c]	3.3 [d]	60	7.0	30.8	9.3	54	1.7

Acres and animals per worker [a]

	Crops and grass	Arable	Wheat	Total cattle	Milch cows	Sheep	Horses
1874	21.3	12.3	2.5	4.2	—	20.7	0.9
1939	44.5	18.1	2.4	12.5	4.0	37.8	1.2
1945	35.0	21.6	4.1 [d]	10.9	3.3	22.7	—

[a] Workers include farmers and laborers and in 1945 about 80,000 members of the Women's Land Army and also prisoners-of-war.
[b] 1943.
[c] United Kingdom.
[d] Including part-time and self-employed.

ery, combined with large farm units, take the lead. But is this efficient farming? Looking again at damage done to the soil since the sods were first turned by the pioneer, often less than a century ago, we may justly say that such agriculture is a hallmark of inefficiency.

STOCK-CARRYING CAPACITY AND STOCK UNITS

The appraisal of agricultural productivity based on acre yield fails to take into account the part played by improved pasture. Out of the total produce of plowed or cropped land more goes to the feeding of animals than to the direct feeding of man. What is the carrying capacity of land in terms of animals? It has become common to attempt to express this in terms of "livestock units." One horse, one cow, one bull, and one bullock are usually each considered as one livestock unit; a heifer or calf is 0.5; a ewe or ram, 0.14; a brood sow, 0.2; a fat pig, 0.1; and 100 adult poultry, one unit.

Well-managed grassland in Britain is considered able to support one grazing unit an acre throughout the year, and it seems permissible to use this as a standard. It can be used also in reverse, i.e. if a country has 10 million livestock units it would require the same number of acres, well managed, to support the number adequately. Increased acre yields resulting from good husbandry refer to grass, fodder crops, and animal-feeding stuffs as much as to foods for direct human consumption and so to increased stock-carrying capacity. True, this may not be reflected at once in increased meat or milk yields in proportion unless the character and quality of the stock is improved at the same time. Incidentally, as Britain has found with the improvement of hill pastures, increased yield of grass is wasted and the pastures rapidly deteriorate unless the animals are present to consume the increase.

Fish as Food

At this point the critic may urge that we have failed to consider the important sources of food in the sea or fresh waters. However, Le Gros Clark's calculations indicate that 98 per cent of our daily energy and 94 per cent of our protein intake are derived from the products of the soil—in other words, that only one or two per cent of our daily energy is derived from the fish we eat. It is of course higher with some nations, notably in the case of the Japanese who are said to derive as much as 5 per cent of their daily energy from fish and perhaps 20 per cent of their protein. Insofar as fish provide a variety to otherwise monotonous cereal diets, they may occupy a special place. The Siamese and the Burmese for example, use their *kapi* or their *ngapi*—a paste made of partly decomposed and strong-smelling fish— to add zip to their rice diet.

Attempts to measure the resources of the sea are beset with difficulties. Exhaustion of some of the great fishing grounds seems clearly proved by lowered yields and the position in respect to whaling for whale oil became so serious that international action was necessary. Breeding of fish for replenishment of both marine and fresh-water fishing grounds has become commonplace, but with what long-term results it cannot be said. With its abundant growth of seaweeds the sea may in the future yield foods not yet used by man.

British and American Farming Compared

It is always well to test the validity of widely held, popular views; they are apt to be misleading in that they fail to present the whole truth. In Britain it is commonly believed that American farms are huge by comparison with British; for instance the much-publicized, extensive wheat farms of the Dakotas are regarded as typical of the whole United States. In traveling for many years through the length and breadth of the land, I have been impressed by the strong hold on United

States farming economy of the small family farm, just as in Britain, and the feeling that these modest units counterbalanced the large holdings of selected areas. I am well aware of the artificial character of an "average" farm obtained by dividing total farm area by numbers of farm units, but as a first approach it offers some useful pointers.

Table XIII brings out the surprising fact that the 5,859,169 farms recorded for 1945 in the United States

TABLE XIII. "AVERAGE FARM" IN THE UNITED STATES
AND IN ENGLAND AND WALES, 1945

(Excluding woodland in farms)

	U.S.	E. and W.
Total area (acres)	167	125
Improved land (crops and grass)	87	99
Cropland	69	60
Cropped	62	60
Plowable or improved pasture	18	39
Unplowable pasture or rough grazing	72	26
Cattle, total	13.3	31.0
Milch cows	4.4	9.4
Work horses	1.6	1.8
Sheep	8.5	65.0
Hogs	10.3	7.0
Farm population	4.3	—
Workers	1.8	2.9

have an average size, if one takes cropland plus plowable pasture as the criterion, of 87 acres against 99 acres of the average full-time holding in England and Wales, of which there are 215,900. It may be that the American figure includes such a large number of part-time or hobby farms—these were eliminated from the British figures—that the comparison is thereby invalidated.

The British practice is to consider 10 acres of rough

TABLE XIV. FARMING EFFICIENCY IN THE UNITED STATES AND THE
UNITED KINGDOM COMPARED, 1945

Per Worker

	Crops and grass acres	Crops acres harvested	Total cattle	Milch cows	Sheep	Hogs	Horses
U. S.	49.1	33.8	7.3	2.5	4.8	5.8	0.9
U. K.	31.0	19.2	9.6	2.9	20.2	2.2	0.6

Per 100 Acres of Cropland and Plowable Pasture

	Workers	Total cattle	Milch cows	Sheep	Hogs	Horses
U. S.	2.0	14.9	5.1	10	12	1.9
U. K.	3.2	21.0	9.4	65	7	1.8

grazing as equivalent to one acre of improved land.
On this basis the "adjusted" acreage of the British farm
is 101 acres and of the American 94, with the British
carrying about 35 stock units and the American about
15. The overall acreage of the American farm, including woodland, is 195 acres, that is 50 per cent larger.
The labor force is 1.8 workers against 2.9 in Britain.
On all the 5,859,000 farms of the United States there
are only 2,115,000 hired workers so that the majority
are obviously run by the farmer himself and his family.
The total number of workers recorded for 1945 was 10,-
431,000, which includes all "family" workers doing 15
or more hours per week without cash wages, while
"hired workers" include all those doing more than one
hour during the week of the survey. On the 216,000
full-time farms of England and Wales there were 625,-
000 workers.

If one adds Scotland and Northern Ireland and all
types of workers in all types of farms the gross number

employed in agriculture is just over a million (1945). This is the figure to be compared with the gross figure of 10,431,000 in the United States.

We have already given above a table showing the increasing efficiency per worker in Britain. If we change the basis by taking gross figures for the whole United Kingdom (i.e. including Northern Ireland and with casual workers but excluding prisoners of war) and the whole United States we get the comparison given in Table XIV. The American worker is responsible for 50 per cent more improved land and harvests 75 per cent more cropland but looks after only about 8.5 stock units against the British worker's 12 units. On balance there is little difference in output per worker.

Another comparison, based on improved land, shows that British farms employ more labor per 100 acres but carry more than double the stock. It should be noted that the British pig population in 1945 was greatly reduced from prewar days, the total being 2,152,000 animals against 4,453,000 in 1937, for the pig is regarded as a "bad converter" of feeding stuffs; hence numbers were deliberately reduced during the war.

THE UNDERDEVELOPED UNITED STATES

In summarizing this chapter we arrive at some surprising conclusions. If output per unit area is taken as the criterion, and we bear in mind the huge world family and its present need for food, maximum agricultural efficiency is exemplified in selected delta regions of China, in Java, and in northwestern Europe. We have

seen how climatic conditions often work against the
farmer in the tropics. We should rather look for universally high yields per acre in the favored temperate-
zone climates. Does this not point to the fact that with
our present knowledge of agricultural production and
of soil management, our present range of crops and of
world food demands, the outstandingly underdeveloped countries of the world are the new lands of the
middle latitudes, including the United States, Argentina, and Canada? Is there any scientific reason why output per acre in these areas should not be brought up
to northwest European levels? Later I shall consider the
national overproduction, which in fact exists, and its
implications.

Already change is taking place. The more accessible
parts of the prairie lands in Canada, the Red River
Basin near Winnipeg, for example, are trending away
from the monoculture of wheat to balanced, mixed
farming, though such change is obviously more difficult
and unlikely to take place in drier areas of precarious
rainfall. A similar trend is obvious in Argentina, notably within the reach of a score of miles or so from the
great capital. Some staggering results would be achieved
if the United States, Canada, and Argentina increased
their output per acre (without increasing area cultivated) up to the levels reached in northwestern Europe.
Against such increases *known* to be possible in mid-
latitudes even the vast potential of the tropics, when we
learn to use the tropical lands, seems to fade into in-
significance.

CHAPTER V

Mining and Minerals

So far we have been dealing with the products of agriculture, products that, broadly speaking, are renewable resources. If land is properly treated it will go on yielding food in perpetuity. When we turn to consideration of the mineral resources of the world the position is entirely different. Contained in the earth's crust are certain stores of those minerals that because of proved value to man we call "economic minerals." Many mineral deposits are deeply buried; many are difficult to locate; some are of great extent; others exist in small quantity, are superficial, and quickly exhausted. Man's first task is to find the deposits, then to work them until exhaustion of the resource puts an end to the enterprise and the associated settlement has to be abandoned or alternative occupations found for its inhabitants. Thus minerals are capital resources won by what is often called "robber" economy.

Renewable and Capital Resources

To some extent, then, it must always be true that mineral resources are a temporary rather than a permanent asset to a country. But this generalization needs qualification. The reserves of certain minerals are so vast that there is little or no possibility of their being exhausted in the foreseeable future. The natural reserves of limestone would seem to assure an ample supply of lime for cement in most countries; and it is doubtful whether any important country is likely to exhaust its reserves of brick-making materials. Many of the known reserves of coal may be expected to last for hundreds, indeed thousands, of years.

There still is an element of luck associated with mineral exploration. Even if the romantic days of the gold rush are past and the hopes of striking an oil gusher become less and less as years go by—though we do not overlook the current spectacular oil discoveries in Alberta—there remain even more significant discoveries of great new ore bodies, such as the iron ores recently located in Labrador and northern Quebec, or the Cerro Bolívar deposit in Venezuela.

Also increasing technical skill renders of value mineral deposits considered worthless in the past. Since an "ore" is technically a deposit from which one or more metals may be profitably extracted, what is not considered an ore one year may become one the next. Old dumps are constantly being worked over for the more effective extraction of gold, silver, or other metals. New smelting processes are permitting the reduction of heretofore unused ores, as copper sulphides at Chuquicamata, Chile. The factor of location also enters in. A good many years ago when I first went to Burma to prospect for oil in the Chindwin River basin, I was very much excited at finding a hill which seemed to be a solid mass of iron ore. It was not of high-grade caliber, as I ascertained by the makeshift means at my command, but still what a discovery! I rode back two days' journey to the nearest telegraph, sent cables to secure a prospecting monopoly, and advised my head office in Rangoon of my action. The reply from headquarters came quickly. It read: "What on earth do you think is the good of iron ore in the Chindwin stop get on with your work." Thus I learned that accessibility is a factor of great importance in assessing the value of an ore deposit.

Finally, there is the enormously significant fact that man is constantly finding new needs for materials previously counted of little or no value. We need scarcely remind ourselves of the sudden importance assumed by ores of radium, and the present importance of uranium and other material used in atomic research. It is not long since aluminum was so difficult to extract from its ores as to be a rare and expensive metal, and the value of magnesium in making light alloys was still unknown. On the tin fields of Malaya the separation of the tin ore from the then useless wolframite was a costly process. With the development of tungsten steels and filaments there came the sudden demand for what had previously been a waste product. Within the present century cadmium, selenium, tantalum, zirconium and other metals have been transformed from curiosities in the chemist's laboratory to substances of commercial importance.

COAL, OIL, AND WATER POWER

First to be considered among the mineral resources are the three main present-day sources of power—coal, oil, and water. Coal, though universally used, is not by any means universal in its occurrence. Coal seams vary from a mere fraction of an inch to 100 or more feet in thickness, though it is customary to ignore seams of less than 1½ feet as impossible to exploit economically. The most numerous seams worked are of the order of 3, 4, or 6 feet in thickness, for the costs of working seams much thicker than 6 feet increase rapidly. Seams are usually constant in thickness over wide areas, so that when a coal field is explored by means of drill holes it is possible to calculate within a relatively small margin of error the total amount of coal actually available. The famous calculations carried out by a Commission of the International Geological Congress of 1913 gave for the first time estimates of the world's coal resources. Naturally the estimates have been modified in many particulars since that date. Tables XV and XVI show some recent figures. In addition to the production of coal and anthracite shown in the tables, there was an output in 1943–47 of an average of 256,000,000 tons of lignite annually. This is mainly important in countries where true coal is scarce; lignite is highly significant in Germany and Czechoslovakia.

In the past, industrial areas tended to grow up on or near the coal fields because of the high cost of transport for a heavy and bulky raw material. For more than a

TABLE XV. ESTIMATED WORLD RESOURCES AND PRODUCTION OF
BITUMINOUS COAL

Reserves in billions of metric tons; production in millions

		Reserves 1937*	Production 1937*	1948†
North America:	Canada	373	12	15
	Mexico	3	1	—
	United States	2,237	449	536
South America:	Brazil	5	1	2
	Chile	—c	2	2
	Colombia	27	—	—
Europe:	Belgium	11	30	27
	Czechoslovakia	31	29	18
	France	14	45	43
	Germany	369	271 b	91
	Hungary	—c	4	1
	Italy	—c	1	1
	Netherlands	7	14	11
	Poland	76	—	70
	Saar	—	—	12.5
	Spain	14	7	10
	U.S.S.R.	1,739	118	201
	United Kingdom	307	244	212
Asia:	China	263	39	9
	India	26	26	31
	Japan	22	42	33
	Korea	6	?	—
	Turkey	2	2	3
Africa:	Nigeria	3	—	0.5
	Southern Rhodesia	4	1	2
	Union of South Africa	216	16	23.5
Oceania:	Australia	17	14	15
	New Zealand	2	2	3
WORLD TOTAL		5,697	1,384 a	1,396 d

* From *Energy Resources of the World*, U.S. Government, 1949.

† From *Minerals Yearbook, 1948*, Washington, 1950.

a Includes lignite expressed as coal equivalent; b including Poland;
c less than half a billion tons (1 billion = 1,000,000,000); d figures for
lignite not included; anthracite in U. S. not included.

The above figures show that the United States has nearly 40 per cent
of known world reserves; Russia, more than 30 per cent; Britain, Germany, and Canada each between 5 and 7 per cent. No country in the
tropics has as much as 1 per cent.

TABLE XVI. WORLD PRODUCTION OF ANTHRACITE, 1943–47

Millions of metric tons

China (est'd.)	1.0	Korea	2.5	Britain	3.7
France (est'd.)	6.0	Morocco	0.2	United States	
French Indochina	0.4	Portugal	0.4	(Penn.)	53.9
Italy	0.1	Spain	1.4	WORLD (est'd.)	114.3

hundred years, however, by destructive distillation, coal has been converted into coke and coal gas and the gas distributed by pipe over considerable areas, thus giving the product a greater flexibility in use than the solid fuel. This same principle has been extended enormously by the use of carbo-electricity—that is electricity generated by the use of coal. The fact that it is economically feasible to distribute electric energy up to and even beyond distances of 300 miles has emancipated many light industries from a coal-field location. But the cost of carbo-electricity, dependent as it is primarily on the extraction of the solid fuel, that is on mining and transport costs, is often high.

With a generally rising standard of living, coal mining has tended to become an increasingly unattractive occupation. Experiments have lately been made looking to elimination of the drudgery of mining. Hydrogenation of coal, whereby it is converted into oil, is an important recent development. Although undertaken primarily to provide countries rich in coal but poor in oil with a liquid fuel, hydrogenation presents possibilities for underground processing that would obviate actual mining.

Mineral oil or petroleum, like coal derived from organic remains of past geological periods, is also found in the sedimentary rocks. Quite probably it originated as small globules scattered through beds of sand, but in the course of time the globules collected, and so we have the phenomenon of oil pools, trapped by a rock structure that prevents escape of the oil to the surface to be dissipated and lost. The task of the oil geologist is to locate the hidden oil pools from the disposition of the rocks and such indications as seepages, which are in fact the escapes of small quantities to the surface.

Two important considerations about oil fields are that each field represents the accumulated resources from a wide, surrounding area and, secondly, that it is impossible to calculate reserves with anything like the accuracy possible for coal. The maintenance of the world's output of oil is dependent on the continued discovery of new fields, and although the pessimists of two or three decades ago have been constantly confounded by new discoveries, we cannot escape the fact that the world demand for oil is still rising and that reserves are certain to be exhausted long before many of the major reserves of coal have been touched. We can go so far as to say that the possession of oil is thus a temporary asset, however valuable. It has, of course, a great advantage over coal in ease of handling through pipe line and by tanker and in convenience of storage.

Unlike the other two sources of power, water is unique in that it is a renewable resource. From early days swift-running streams were used to turn water wheels and to drive machinery, and there still are parts of the world where water wheels are in operation, grinding corn or sawing wood. Broadly speaking when one talks of water power at the present day one refers to the manufacture of electricity by means of falling water passing through turbines. In the generation of water power there are certain prerequisites: a constant steady source of water and an adequate fall in level. These conditions are most obviously satisfied in mountainous countries of abundant, well-distributed precipitation, winter temperatures not low enough to freeze water, and facilities for construction of storage reservoirs. Provided there is a large gathering ground and hence a large body of water, it is not necessary to have a fall of any great height. The important Shannon power scheme for Ireland, for example, utilizes a fall of about 100 feet from the level of the Shannon River in the central plateau of Ireland to approximately sea level, where the works are situated.

Those countries which have facilities for the development of hydroelectric power have thus a permanent asset, and it may be that in the long run they will be the fortunate ones.

The great importance in the world today of coal, oil, and water power is apt to lead us to forget the existence of other sources of power. Wood is still widely used as a fuel, either as it is or as charcoal; and here, too, we have a renewable resource still valuable in many parts of the world. Despite many proposals, little use has yet been made of the constant movement of the tides of the ocean as a stable source of power or of the sun's energy. Now a new source is on the horizon; but how soon the results of modern atomic research will be used for power production remains to be seen.

Taking the world as a whole, therefore, we have little cause to fear power famine, though the relative significance of our present sources is almost bound to change.

Fuel and Power in the Underdeveloped Lands

In preceding chapters stress has been laid on the supreme necessity of securing adequate food for the peoples of the world. It is idle to pretend that development could, or should, stop at that one objective. Even the simple end of an adequate and a sufficiently varied diet cannot be achieved without fuel for cooking. Very quickly development comes to include a decent standard of housing—adequate heating and lighting, water supply, and sanitation. We of the Western world have witnessed a world evolving from a coal age, through a gas age, to the day when a public supply of electric energy is almost regarded as part of the individual's birthright. In the underdeveloped areas it must be a plunge straight into the electric age. The touch of a switch which means a good cheap light, a motor in action for a thousand jobs (not the least being the pumping of a supply of good water), the control through electric refrigeration over the preservation of nearly all types of food—these must be a primary aim of development even if crude fuels continue to be used for cooking and heating.

What, then, are the resources of fuel and power in the underdeveloped lands?

Table XV of the world's coal resources and coal production shows concentration in a few areas. In the New World, the vast resources and output of coal in the United States and, to a lesser degree, in Canada contrast with the poverty of the whole of Latin America. Naturally one asks the question, how far is this just lack of knowledge—that deposits have not yet been located? For reasons related to geological structure which will be considered later, we may regard Latin America's poverty in coal as a proven fact—it is unlikely that any sizeable undiscovered fields exist.

The distribution of coal in the Eastern Hemisphere is equally irregular. In Europe there is the belt of rich fields stretching from Britain through northern France, Belgium, Holland, Germany, Poland, and Czechoslovakia into Russia and a few fields outside, as in northern Spain, but little elsewhere. There is no doubt that the U.S.S.R. both in Europe and Asia has vast coal fields; China's reserves, though much less extensive than once believed, are large, and so are India's. Japan is less fortunate; with the exception of Turkey, other Asiatic countries also have but little coal. Australia has at least one really large field of good coal and others of economic importance. In Africa a large and valuable field exists in the Union of South Africa, but over the vast stretches of underdeveloped tropical Africa there is little or no coal, even allowing for the Nigerian deposits and others in Sierra Leone and Tanganyika which are moderate-quality lignites.

If, therefore, we are thinking of the underdeveloped

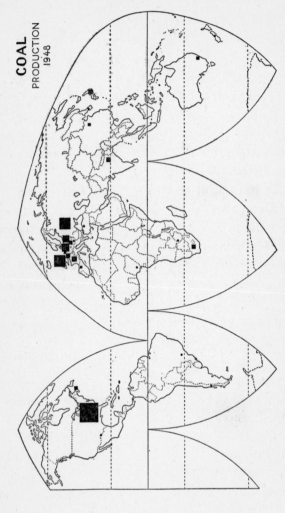

Fig. 27. The principal coal-producing countries; compare Table XV. Much of South America, Africa, and Australia lacks coal reserves.

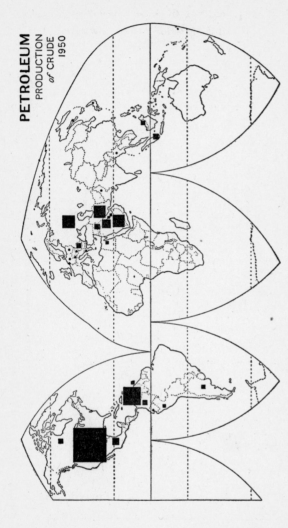

PETROLEUM
PRODUCTION
of CRUDE
1950

Fig. 28. The principal sources of petroleum, 1950; compare Table XVII.

TABLE XVII. WORLD PRODUCTION OF CRUDE PETROLEUM, 1950*

In millions of barrels of 42 U.S. gallons

			Per cent
North America:	Canada	29	0.8
	Mexico	72	1.9
	Trinidad	20	0.7
	United States	1,973	52.2
South America:	Argentina	23	0.6
	Colombia	34	0.9
	Ecuador	2.5	—
	Peru	15	0.4
	Trinidad	20	0.5
	Venezuela	542	14.4
Europe:	Albania	2	—
	Austria	6	0.2
	Germany	8	0.2
	Hungary	3.5	0.1
	Netherlands	5	0.1
	Poland	1	—
	Rumania	32	0.8
	U.S.S.R.	263	7.0
Asia:	Bahrain	11	0.3
	British Borneo	30	0.8
	Burma	0.5	—
	India and Pakistan	4.5	0.1
	Iran	240	6.3
	Iraq	47	1.2
	Japan	2	—
	Kuwait	125	3.3
	Netherlands East Indies	50	1.3
	Sakhalin	7	0.2
	Sarawak	30	0.8
	Saudi Arabia	200	5.3
	Qatar	11	0.3
Africa:	Egypt	16	0.4
WORLD TOTAL		3,780	

* *World Oil*, Feb. 15, 1951, p. 238.

areas in the world as those lying primarily within the tropics, coal is unlikely to play a substantial part in their development.

With petroleum the position is somewhat different.

The great oil fields of South America have brought wealth and rapid change to Venezuela, Colombia, Ecuador, and Peru; and they have projected the limelight onto Bolivia and Paraguay. In the Old World, oil discoveries and exploitations of Iran, Iraq, Arabia, parts of the East Indies, and to a less extent central Burma have brought about extensive economic development.

On the other hand, it becomes increasingly doubtful whether petroleum will ever play a large part in the development of tropical Africa. The only known oil fields of Africa are the small ones, with decreasing output, on the Suez Coast of Egypt, a new one in Sinai, and small ones in the Atlas lands.[1]

So we turn to water as the source of power destined to play the larger part in the development of the underdeveloped lands of Africa and other parts of the tropics.

Here in the tropical forests, especially in Central and West Africa, are the greatest untapped sources of potential water power. Small developments in the Belgian Congo and plans for exploiting the Upper Nile and the Volta are but forerunners of other possibilities.

Nothing is deserving of closer study than water resources—and it is far more than a question of hydroelectricity, important as that may be. As I have already stated, I believe that the control of water is the key to development in tropical lands.

GEOLOGICAL STRUCTURE AND MINERAL DEPOSITS

Water power depends on the circumstances of precipitation as well as on the form of the ground. As far as other mineral resources are concerned, no such direct relationship exists as that between water power and climate. Like all generalized statements this needs some qualification. In the more arid parts of the world, where salts are derived from deposits at or near the surface, as the sodium nitrate of Chile, or from salt lakes such as the Dead Sea, they may be said to owe their existence to the aridity of the climate. But such cases do not render invalid the broad general statement that mineral deposits depend on geological structure and not on climate.

The geological structure of any part of the earth's surface is the result of many millions of years of the earth's evolution. It is something fixed and definite; the mineral resources of any country are an endowment provided by nature not to be changed or varied by man. The use which a country may make of its mineral deposits will, of course, depend on many factors, notably the country's resources in men, materials, and money. But whatever the stage of development, the fact remains that the mineral resources are there or are not there, as the case may be. The possession of minerals to some extent redresses the balance between the nations, and some that are unfortunate in their climatic conditions are fortunate in their mineral resources.

PRESENT AND FUTURE MINERAL PRODUCTION

Minerals, it might be said, have provided the world with that element of chance that appeals to the gambling instinct in mankind. Whereas the production of

food and other agricultural raw materials results in a
settled or slowly changing pattern of farms, villages and
towns, the exploitation of minerals results in an unstable pattern of human settlement, sometimes liable
to violent and rapid changes. To take a well-known instance, gold was discovered in the remote Yukon in
1895, more than five hundred miles from the nearest
town on the coast of the Pacific. When the news leaked
out, the Gold Rush began. And today the magic words
the "Trail of '98" remain to perpetuate the extraor-
dinary migration of thousands of prospectors to Skagway, up over the Chilkoot Pass, later by the White Pass,
to Bennett, and thence by lake and river down the
Yukon to Dawson City. Skagway leapt in population
from virtually nothing to several thousand in a matter
of weeks; Bennett, too. One of the most breath-taking
mountain railways in the world was built in a matter of
months. When the placer deposits gave out almost as
suddenly as they had been developed, Skagway became
a ghost town, though it has had several new leases of
life, and Bennett reverted to a waste of scrubland, with
a derelict wooden church and a railway station; and the
Gold Rush railway now extracts its gold from the
pockets of summer tourists.

There are ghost towns in the western United States,
such as Arizona's famed Tombstone, and in Australia,
where Bendigo and Ballarat live in public memory
more through the stories of Sherlock Holmes than
through their former importance as gold producers.
And so in many other parts of the world.

We see the same thing happening with oil. But outside Britain it is more difficult to realize that the same phenomena are being witnessed on the British coal fields. And even in Britain this particular problem has scarcely yet been faced. Coal was worked in the Newcastle area of the Northumbrian and Durham coal field at least as early as the fourteenth century; in its western part, where the seams reach the surface, the coal has been actively worked for a century and a half and the field is largely exhausted. But over that period there have grown up not only colliery villages but also towns of considerable size, equipped with public utilities and all the paraphernalia of civic life. Were it not for such substantial developments and the investments that they represent, these towns of the exhausted coal field would also be ghost towns. The reason for their existence has now disappeared. What of their future? Are they to be allowed to decay and die by inches, or should positive planning step in and, by encouraging new forms of industrial development, revitalize the area? This is a problem common to many of the older industrial areas of Europe which grew up originally on coal fields.

In considering this question we must not confuse the older exhausted or partly exhausted sections of the coal fields with the vigorous life of those parts now being actively developed. Many writers, particularly American writers, have fallen into the error of believing that British coal is becoming exhausted. It certainly is not, but it is becoming exhausted in certain of the older parts of the fields.

The phenomena of discovery, development, decay, death, universally characteristic of mineral deposits and mining settlements, are evident all over the world. Graphs of mineral production, particularly of the metalliferous minerals which occur in veins liable to peter out and disappear in depth, show wide fluctuations. People do not eat minerals. Whereas the demand for food is relatively stable, minerals yielding material for the manufacture of capital equipment or consumer goods are liable to be affected much more by periods of depression and suffer much more from price fluctuations. In times of prosperity, mining is active; in times of depression, mines close down. This is another reason why mining communities are unstable. Any economic geographer knows how difficult it is to keep up to date when one is discussing mineral resources and mineral production of a particular country. What is a true statement today may be false tomorrow. What is rightly described one year as the largest gold mine in the whole North American continent may be flooded and abandoned within twelve months—as actually happened at Juneau. It is almost impossible to talk in specific terms about the potential production of minerals. What we do know, however, is that immense possibilities still exist in the world, in geologically unexplored ancient rocks of Brazil and Africa, for instance. In some cases it may be that superficial deposits render the task of discovery difficult by hiding with a thick blanket what lies underneath. In other cases it is the remoteness of unexplored areas, such as the heart of Brazil, or the far north of Canada, which has prevented exploration, discovery, and development.

It was no fault of the early prospectors, usually without maps and armed only with primitive equipment that they failed to find deposits which can now be detected by new methods. Outline geological maps can be prepared from air photographs, even before the area is visited by a ground party; geophysical methods permit detection of ore bodies even deeply buried.

There is no doubt that many countries at present regarded as unimportant are destined to leap into worldwide significance as their mineral resources become known.

The International Role of Mining

This leads to a consideration of the way in which minerals may redress the balance between nations. In so far as a country lies within a certain type of climate, its agricultural development must take place along certain lines, and its potential production can in many respects be calculated or forecast. Similarly by virtue of the climate and the build or relief of the country the areas capable of cultivation, of afforestation, of being developed for water power, are either known or can be readily surveyed. Minerals and mining provide the unknown quantities and may give us the surprises of the future. Even countries which have long had detailed geological and mineralogical surveys are found to have unexpected resources. During World War II an oilfield of considerable value was located and worked in England while the borings for oil revealed remarkably rich deposits of potassium and other salts previously unsuspected. It may even be that whereas countries are left to work out their own salvation in the matter of feeding themselves, international trade must continue so long as certain minerals are essential in our modern existence. I shall discuss later the remarkable trend so evident in the United States for the finding of substitutes for most things in life, and it may be urged that where we now regard certain metals as of vital importance substitutes may be found in the future. Yet it is difficult to see how minerals can be robbed entirely of their great international role.

This role is an ancient one. Throughout history minerals have played a decisive part not only in the rise and fall of great powers but in the successive development of previously underdeveloped areas. Salt was one of the earliest minerals both to promote international trade and to provoke wars. To this day the word "salary" reminds us that it referred originally to money paid to a Roman soldier to buy the all important *sal* (salt).

It would seem that the earliest of the traders to come from the continent of Europe to the shores of the British Isles came in order to secure some of the gold ornaments then made from the long since exhausted gold deposits of North Wales and Ireland. For many centuries before Christ the trade of the Mediterranean, the heart of the known world, was dominated by Cretan and Phoenician metal merchants who shipped copper from Cyprus, gold, silver, and copper from Spain, and later tin from Cornwall in Britain. It was the silver of Spain which enabled Carthage to hire mercenaries to fight the Romans. When Carthage was driven from Spain by the Romans it was the possession of these mineral spoils that enabled Rome to become the great world power of the day. She secured gold, silver, copper, and iron from Spain; invaded and conquered Britain for lead and silver and copper and tin; and subdued Greece for more silver and copper. Historians ascribe the decline and fall of the Roman Empire to various causes; some see it in the over-development of the civil service; some trace it to the dwindling supplies of metals.

Be that as it may, the story has been repeated many times since. The discovery of the New World itself by Columbus was part of the quest for the gold, precious stones, and other treasures of the Indies and the incredible half-century of Spanish conquest that followed was dictated essentially by the lust of the *conquistadores* for gold and silver. Sea power passed to Britain when her ships seized the treasure-laden Spanish galleons on the high seas and shortly after defeated the Armada.

With the coming of the industrial revolution it was England's possession of large deposits of coal suitable for coking and of iron ore and limestone flux in close proximity that laid the foundation of her world leadership in the nineteenth century.

The last century has but quickened the pace. Gold accidentally discovered in California in 1848 led to the rush of '49 and so to the opening up and settlement of the almost unknown western half of the continent. In 1851 the discovery of gold in Australia led to the migration of more than a million Britishers to what had been previously a despised "convict settlement." In 1867 the discovery of diamonds at Kimberley and a few years later of the world's richest gold field on the Rand led not only to the development of South Africa but really to the whole "opening up" of Africa and to the scramble for African territory by Britain, France, Belgium, and Germany. Copper brought both railway and settlers to the Belgian and Rhodesian Katanga. Rhodesia, named for the British pioneer, Cecil John Rhodes, was itself explored and established by profits from mining in South Africa.

In the present century it is the liquid gold, petroleum, that has come to the fore as a factor in economic and political circumstance. The discovery of the oil fields of the Maracaibo Basin has caused profound changes in the economic life of Venezuela. It was not the possibility of food production in the Chaco which underlay the boundary dispute between Bolivia and Paraguay and led to the war of 1933–34, but the possibility of oil. The search for oil actuated the exploration of little-known Borneo and New Guinea. Perhaps the most staggering modern development of all is the sudden transformation of the poverty-stricken sheikdoms of the Persian Gulf to positions of worldly affluence and international significance—all since 1932 when oil was struck in Bahrain Island, with the geologists still living who had reported the area worthless.

At this very moment the newly-located iron ore deposits of Ungava and northern Quebec are directly responsible for the railway now being constructed from the St. Lawrence and the "opening up" of new lands. The past three years have seen a significant change in the whole of Canada's economy through the Alberta oil strikes. In 1948 Canada imported thirty-three million barrels of oil from the United States, but it is expected that the country will shortly be able to supply her domestic needs as well as be in a position to export.[2]

All this affords justification for the statement that minerals still provide a main incentive for man's interest in underdeveloped lands; still provide the surprise element; still underlie national stability and development; still involve international rivalry and, whether we like it or not, exploitation by the strong.

Even the largest of the world's political units cannot claim to be self-sufficient in the full range of minerals and metals required in our modern civilization. Probably the U.S.S.R. approaches most nearly to self-sufficiency; on the other hand the United States, despite an overwhelmingly strong position in many directions, lacks certain essential mineral commodities and is rapidly exhausting her known reserves of others. This was, in part, the theme of Dr. Isaiah Bowman's survey "The Geographical Situation of the United States in Relation to World Policies," presented before the Royal Geographical Society in 1948.

MINERALS AND UNDERDEVELOPED AREAS

It is instructive to review the world sources of some of the leading metals. Thereby is emphasized the dependence of the great powers on otherwise underdeveloped areas. It may be that certain underdeveloped areas will be able to pay for their own development. As Sir Frank Stockdale pointed out in a survey of recent British Colonial developments [3] shortly before his sudden death, "most mining developments have taken place at the instance of private enterprise." The interest of governments is a comparatively new development.

Aluminum, as the oxide alumina, is a constituent of all clays and one of the most abundant metals in the earth's crust, but the bulk of the product is obtained from the not very common bauxite. Since cheap electric power, usually hydroelectric, is needed for the high temperatures of the reduction furnaces, the ore is brought to the power. In the interwar years, Germany and Canada (following the United States) were two of the chief producers of aluminum, and they imported almost all the bauxite they needed. Canada derived most of her supply of the ore from British Guiana, which alone produced nearly 2,000,000 tons of the ore; Dutch Guiana (Surinam) overtook British Guiana in 1947 and in that year the two Guianas alone furnished nearly one-half of the world's total supply. Other sources of bauxite include the Gold Coast and the Netherlands East Indies, and so we have a perfect example of underdeveloped

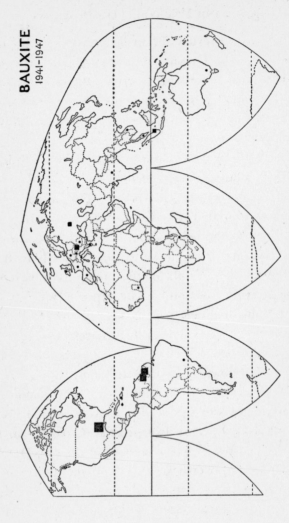

BAUXITE
1941–1947

Fig. 29. The chief sources of bauxite, 1941–1947.

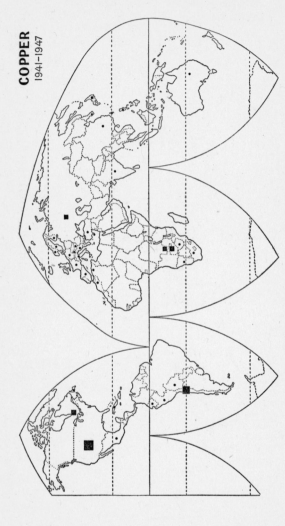

COPPER
1941–1947

Fig. 30. The chief sources of copper ore, 1941–1947.

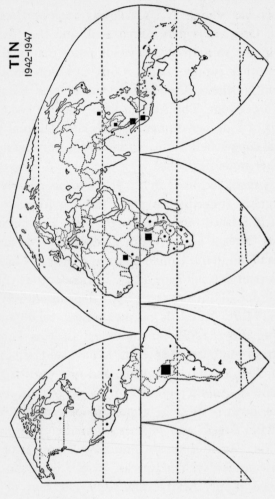

TIN
1942–1947

Fig. 31. The chief sources of tin, 1942–1947.

tropical lands making a major contribution to the economy of the Western world.

Copper has shown an enormously increased world demand. Ores are widely distributed, and the United States, in the western states, yields more than a third of the world's supply (1948); Chile produces about a fifth; and Northern Rhodesia and the Belgian Katanga about 16 per cent. The African field, with its 500,000,-000 tons of four per cent ore is the largest actual and potential copper belt in the world, and it is in the heart of another underdeveloped area.

Tin is more localized in its distribution. Nearly all tin is smelted from the heavy and stable oxide, cassiterite, which, washed out of its parent lode, is commonly found as "stream tin" in alluvial deposits. Practically no tin is found in the United States and little in Canada, and less than two per cent of the world's output comes from Europe. Thus the chief users depend entirely on imports. More than half of the present total (1948), excluding the U.S.S.R., about which little is known, comes from southeast Asia—from Malaya and adjoining parts of Siam and Lower Burma, and two small islands of Indonesia. Another quarter of world output comes from the heart of Bolivia, important percentages from the Belgian Congo and Nigeria, a smaller percentage from China. Again the main sources of supply are from otherwise underdeveloped areas. In all, the countries mentioned supply nearly ninety-five per cent of the total.

Tungsten is also restricted in its occurrence. In 1913

Burma led world production, followed by the United States and Portugal. World War I stimulated production, and China, Korea, and Bolivia were added to the list of producers. The great importance of tungsten in the manufacture of high tension steels led to an intensive search for new sources of supply during the Second World War, though with limited success. Today the list of substantial producers also includes Brazil and Tasmania.

Other ferroalloys of importance are nickel and manganese. About four-fifths of all nickel comes from Canada, one-sixth from Russia, and most of the remainder from the French Pacific island of New Caledonia. Russia is far in the lead in world output of manganese, followed by the Gold Coast, India, South Africa, and Brazil; production has declined in Cuba since the close of the war and has risen in French Morocco.

Radium is, of course, a rare metal, and so are workable ores of uranium, of which it is a disintegration product. The discovery of the radium-uranium ore of Great Bear Lake in Canada's Northwest Territories in 1930 well illustrates how a single mineral deposit can completely alter the whole world picture. The other chief producer is the Belgian Congo. It is unnecessary to comment on the feverish search for deposits now being prosecuted all over the world.

More than a quarter of all the world's antimony, important in type metal, flameproofed textiles, and other industrial uses, comes from Bolivia. Peru is the world's largest producer of bismuth. Southern Rhodesia and

South Africa together take a leading part (one-third) in the world production of chromium ore, of which there are also important deposits in New Caledonia, the Philippines, Cuba, and Turkey. Practically the whole of the world's cobalt is produced by the Belgian Congo, Northern Rhodesia, and French Morocco, with smaller quantities from Canada and the United States.

A nonmetallic mineral of much interest is asbestos. The bulk of the world's supply comes from eastern Canada, followed by Southern Rhodesia, the Union of South Africa, and the little British protectorate of Swaziland. Africa is *par excellence* the home of the diamond—the Union of South Africa, Southwest Africa, Sierra Leone, the Belgian Congo, and the Gold Coast. The spectacular discovery of diamonds in· Tanganyika changed considerably the economic position of that territory.

With metals whose ores are more widely distributed we may note the important part played by the remoter regions of the world—the gold of Southern Rhodesia, the Belgian Congo, and West Africa, the silver-lead of the Bawdwin mines of Burma, the silver of the Peruvian and Bolivian Andes and the Belgian Congo. The position of iron ore is particularly interesting. Although iron is very widely distributed in the earth's crust, it is only when the content of metallic iron reaches a certain proportion that minerals or rocks become "iron ore." Many low-grade iron ores are only worked if they are easily accessible or if the countries concerned have no better supplies. The great European producers have come to rely more and more on imported ores and once again underdeveloped areas have or may have an important part to play. For example, iron ore is now shipped from Algeria and Sierra Leone to Britain.

The present trend is for governments to take a large part in the work of survey and exploration. The Australian government pioneered with geophysical reconnaissance surveys, the Canadian government with the use of air surveys. The British Colonial Office has set up a Colonial Geological Survey where the small British personnel available is aided by American geologists. The first issue of its bulletin *Colonial Geology and Mineral Resources* appeared in 1950. The results of the survey's work are unpredictable both in incidence and magnitude, but there is little doubt that minerals are destined to play a large part in future development—to the lasting benefit, let us hope, both of the countries concerned and of the world as a whole.

CHAPTER VI

Salvaging the Old World

Most of the countries of Europe and many other parts of the Old World have the same basic problem—how to use small areas of land to the best advantage of large populations. Some of these countries are very nearly able to feed themselves. France, with a total area of 136,252,800 acres, of which 46,000,000 are plowed, another 30,000,000 in pasture, and 5,000,000 in special crops, vineyards, etc., is able to produce the bulk of the food required by the 41,500,000 inhabitants. The surplus of such products as wines, spirits, cheeses, and fruits balances to a considerable extent the import of foodstuffs of tropical origin.

In Italy the situation is much less favorable. The estimated mid-1947 population was 45,373,000 on an area of 74,400,000 acres, much of it, however, of little use. If the wide plains of the Po are excellently adapted to cultivation, in peninsular Italy the land is patchy in quality, ranging from some rich volcanic soils, through dry limestones, to marshes, and suffering from the vagaries of the Mediterranean climate. The Italian farmer has been praised as the finest in the world; his industry is clearly seen in his elaborate terracing of the steep hillsides of the south. But in the entire country only 32,000,000 acres are in arable land, 5,800,000 in tree and bush crops, a cultivated area of little more than eight-tenths of an acre a head; and, even if we add the 13,000,000 acres in meadow and pasture, the total productive land is still only just over an acre a head. There is a considerable export of specialized produce—fruits, wines, cheeses—but basic foodstuffs, notably wheat, must be imported. Many of the people, particularly the city dwellers, live in such poverty, so near to actual hunger, as to invite a politically dangerous situation; a people turning to fascism for salvation in one decade, tempted by communism in the next.

The situation in Denmark is in marked contrast. This country was truthfully described in old geographical textbooks as one of the smallest and poorest in Europe—with no minerals, no sources of power, and for the most part with poor glacial soils. The soils have been carefully built up by the use of leguminous crops, fertilizers, and animal manures (enriched by the use of imported corn for feeding) so that now Denmark on 10 ½ million acres, five-sevenths productive farmland, supports more than 4 million people, some of the best fed in the world, and has a large export of dairy produce.

The value placed by European nations on land as the one permanent, ultimate, tangible asset of the people is illustrated by the efforts of the Netherlanders to extend their cultivated and cultivable area by enclosing and draining the Zuyder Zee so that there now are 6 million acres for 10 million people or three-fifths of an acre per head of productive farmland. The cost of reclamation, estimated at $600 an acre, is about three to four times the value in the open market of the reclaimed land as agricultural land.

In Britain there is unfortunately no Zuyder Zee to be reclaimed, and any addition to the land surface by the enclosure and drainage of tidal flats can be of restricted areas only. Nevertheless, reclamation of flats and drainage of old fens or "mosses" has been going on for at least two thousand years and may still be seen in progress when nature has prepared the ground. In recent years new techniques have been devised—as in the introduction of rice grass (*Spartina*) to colonize tidal mud.

Even with the maximum application of science to agricultural production, the highly industrialized countries of the Old World must remain far from self-sufficient in food staples. This is, of course, notably the case in Britain, and Britain we shall take as the chief illustration for this chapter on land-use planning.

NATIONAL LAND PLANNING IN BRITAIN

England, Wales, and Scotland comprise about 56 million acres, with a population approaching 50 million. In England and Wales alone a land area of 37 million acres must serve the needs of a population of 44 million, that is approximately 0.85 of an acre a head. However, only about 24 million acres is improved farmland, representing only a little more than half an acre per

capita. This improved farmland comprises both plow-
land or cropland and that type of farmland so characteristic of England, permanent enclosed grassland.

The planning problem in Britain is complicated by
the highly complex pattern of use already in existence,
an old rural pattern upon which is superimposed a
pattern created by the industrial revolution with its
early dependence on coal fields and its development of
great manufacturing towns. The whole objective of the
planning program is to secure a proper allocation of
land for the varied needs of the people. For simplifica-
tion, needs are grouped in six basic categories: the need
of work, which puts the location of industry into the
forefront; the need of a home, which involves land for
housing; the need of food, which means conservation
of the good agricultural land for food production and
at the same time the development of poorer land for
production of timber and other raw materials; the need
for transportation and communications, including new
main motor highways and airports; and finally the need
for defense, which involves the allocation of land for
training purposes to the Fighting Services.

The present development of town and country planning in Britain is sometimes mistakenly regarded as a
development for which the Labour Government, elected
in 1945, was responsible. This is not so. Land planning
has been forced upon Britain by circumstances independent of political considerations.

In the years between the First and Second World
Wars, agriculture in Britain was a depressed industry

and it received little consideration from the government. At that time Britain was still enjoying the advantages of her accumulated investments overseas and had also a large proportion of the world's carrying trade and of the world's financial and insurance business. As a result there was an automatic flow into the country of foodstuffs and raw materials which represented payment of interest, or payment for services rendered. It seemed then, as it had seemed for the preceding century, as if home production of foodstuffs was unimportant and in any case it was difficult for the British farmer with a high standard of living to compete with the "cheap" food sent from abroad, often at under cost of production and at the expense of "mining" the soil. In consequence, the use of land was determined by the highest bidder, irrespective of quality. As a result, between 1929 and 1938 farmland was being lost to various forms of constructional development at the net rate of 60,000 acres a year. Good farmland is usually well drained and level or gently undulating; hence it is usually the most suitable for industrial development and the most easily developed for housing, and so the land lost to agriculture was mainly of the better or even the best quality.

Toward the end of the interwar period two things had become so obvious as to attract the serious attention of the government. The first was the concentration of industry in the heart of the country, particularly in Greater London, Greater Birmingham and Coventry, and the towns of south Lancashire. In particular,

Greater London was growing at such a rate that half of all the new factories established in the interwar years were in that area, with attendant difficulties of transport and communication. This central belt, it is true, was prospering and yielding large sums in tax revenue; but at the same time in the older industrial areas on the periphery—in Scotland, in the northeast (Northumberland and Durham), in the northwest (Cumberland coalfield), and the South Wales coalfield—depression and widespread unemployment were rife, and what the government received from the prosperous center it was paying out to the depressed periphery. A Royal Commission on the Geographical Distribution of the Industrial Population was set up, under the chairmanship of Sir Montague Barlow, to enquire into the situation. In due course it recommended encouragement to industry to spread itself more widely, in other words a planned dispersal of industry.

The other governmental worry was the despoiling of the rural landscape. The output of food was diminishing at the same time that the sprawl of industry was destroying the amenities of the countryside. Now the townsman enjoys his country, and the beauties of England have long been a source of wealth to the country in attracting overseas visitors. Tourists do not come to see ugly rows of red brick villas and bungalows. So a Committee on Land Utilisation in Rural Areas under the chairmanship of Lord Justice Scott was set up. The terms of reference of this committee are worth quoting: "To consider the conditions which should govern building and other constructional development in country areas consistently with the maintenance of agriculture, and in particular the factors affecting the location of industry, having regard to economic operation, part-time and seasonal employment, the well-being of rural communities and the preservation of rural amenities."

It is not necessary here to enter into the financial aspects involved. Basically the problem is that known as compensation and betterment. If a man in the interests of good planning is prevented from building on his land, or developing it as he would wish, he is surely entitled to some compensation. If new development takes place on neighboring land, which thus automatically acquires an enhanced value, its owner should be subjected to a betterment charge. Theoretically what is collected in "betterment" from the one should pay what is due to the other in "compensation," taking the country as a whole. The problem of compensation and betterment might be solved by nationalizing the land, but by and large this drastic step is abhorrent to the average Britisher.

On the basis of these and other reports, the government began to put planning in action. A Departmental Ministry of Town and Country Planning was established, charged with the task of coordination, but at the same time it placed a responsibility on existing government departments to do their own forward thinking. Thus the Board of Trade was made responsible for directing the location of industry; the Ministry of Agriculture was given the task of safeguarding agricultural land, and "clearance" by its officers is required before land can be developed for housing or industry; the Ministry of Transport was charged with the preparation of schemes for new motor roads; the Ministry of Education drew its plans for improved schools with large playing fields; the Service Departments put forward their demands for training grounds, air fields, etc. Other ministries came into the picture—the Ministry of Health, responsible for housing and concerned also with water supply. The Ministry of Town and Country Planning, in addition to its task of coordination, became concerned with the siting of proposed new towns. (A change was made early in 1951 to Ministry of Local Government and Planning, with responsibility for housing. A further change resulted in October, 1951, with the return of a Conservative Government.) This setup applied to England and Wales only; Scotland is dealt with separately, but the broad pattern is the same.

The work is governed mainly by two recent Acts of Parliament: the Agriculture Act of 1947, which among other things provides the farmer with a guaranteed market for his products and prices fixed in advance, and the Town and Country Planning Act, 1947, which governs the general principles of town planning.

It should be emphasized that planning as a whole is in the experimental stage. Among the problems now being faced is that of competition between agencies. Each urges its own particular scheme, and, in the aggregate, projects become impossible because of limitations of area. In some calculations which I presented in a recent paper on "Planning and Agriculture," [1] I noted the effect of adopting throughout the country modern standards of housing density, recreation areas, new roads, and other requirements of land. The minimum acreage required for urban development of what is at present open land is 713,000; on more generous lines, advocated by many town planners, the acreage is placed at up to 2,250,000 acres or ten per cent of existing farm land. If these standards of low-density rehousing are adopted, there is the danger that one-sixth of the whole surface of England and Wales may be built up.

Many cities and towns in Britain, especially those suffering severely from war damage, as well as some larger regions, have prepared more or less elaborate "plans." How far these will be followed is another matter—dependent on decisions of the local government authority concerned, central government approval, availability of material and capital, and many other factors. Under the Town and Country Planning Act, however, every county is required to draw up for submission to and approval by the Minister of Town and Country Planning an outline of development for the whole county area. Britain is thus committed to nation-wide, compulsory land-use planning.

SOME RESULTS OF THE BRITISH EXPERIMENTS

If we accept as a working hypothesis that it is the duty of each of the lands of the Old World to attempt to work out its own salvation within the broad framework of international cooperation, it may be of value to put on record some results of the British experiments.

In the first place is the necessity for a firm, factual foundation. Since all planning of land use must start from the present position, we require to know what that present position is and as far as possible the reasons for it. It was with this in mind that in 1930 I organized the Land Utilisation Survey of Britain, with the object of recording the then existing use of every acre in England, Wales, and Scotland. The work, very largely carried out by an army of volunteers from the universities and schools, was recorded on some 22,000 sheets of the Ordnance Survey's 6-inch map, that is the map on the scale of 1:10,560. The classification was a simple one. The prime categories, most of which were subdivided, were:

F   Forest and woodland
M   Meadowland and permanent grass
A   Arable or tilled land, fallow, rotation grass and market gardens
H   Heathland, moorland, commons and rough hill pasture
G   Gardens, allotments, nurseries, etc.
O   Orchards
W   Land agriculturally unproductive, e.g. buildings, yards, mines, cemeteries, etc.
P   Ponds, lakes, reservoirs, ditches, dikes, streams, and anything containing water.

After the field work had been reduced for publication to the scale of one inch to one mile, an explanation of the complex pattern which the maps displayed was essayed. This was done in a series of explanatory memoirs, one for each county. The completed work appeared in nine volumes entitled *The Land of Britain*. I summarized it in my book *The Land of Britain: Its Use and Misuse* (1948). Suffice it to say that the factors operating to produce the land-use pattern were found to be partly physical, that is elevation, relief, drainage, soils, climate (especially rainfall); partly historical, such as incidence of ownership and the early establishment of settlements; and partly economic, the effects of agricultural prices, labor costs, transportation facilities, and so on.

The work, by showing the existence of certain trends in usage, served as a basis for planning, for planning is in essence either the encouragement of trends, where they are deemed to be right, or their reversal, where they are deemed to be wrong. There is no doubt that positive land planning is doomed to fail unless it utilizes the favorable factors provided by nature. It is clear, for example, that the location of much heavy industry—the extractive industries of coal mining and iron-ore mining, iron and steel, ship building—is determined by physical factors. Though the operation of physical factors may be less apparent in other industries or in other aspects of land use, they are nonetheless universally present and need to be understood.

In the second place is the need of more factual knowledge. When government machinery for planning was established, and Planning Consultants or County Planning Officers began to draw up their outline plans for submission to the central government, gaps in knowledge were everywhere apparent. We talked about preserving good agricultural land, but the definition of good agricultural land was not to be found, and certainly no attempt had been made to map its occurrence.

A Scheme of Land Classification

A first task was to draw up a scheme of land classification not, be it noted, exactly in terms of "good," "medium," and "poor" but rather of types, since what is the "best" agricultural land for certain crops is certainly not the best for others. In simplified form the tenfold classification is as follows:

Category I—Good Quality Land

Highly productive when under good management. Land in this category has the following characteristics: Site. 1, not too elevated; 2, level, gently sloping or undulating; 3, favorable aspect. Soil. 1, deep; 2, favorable water conditions (actual or potential); 3, texture mostly loams but including some peats, sands, silts, and clays.

1 *First Class Land Capable of Intensive Cultivation.* This land is especially good for the cultivation of foodstuffs for human consumption and hence designated 1(A) where A indicates "arable." The soils are deep and in texture are mainly loams, but include some peats, fine sands, silts, and loamy clays. Drainage must be free but not excessive, and the soils must not be excessively stony and must work easily at all seasons.

2 *Good General Purpose Farmland.* This land is similar to No. 1, but has less depth of soil; presence of

stones; occasional liability to drought or wetness; or some limitation of the seasons when soil works easily results in a restriction of the range of usefulness. When the conditions are such that the land is particularly suitable for arable cultivation the designation 2(A) may be used; when the conditions are such that sown grasses or permanent grassland are particularly suitable, the designation 2 (AG) may be used, where G indicates "grass."

3 *First Class Land with Water Conditions Especially Favoring Grass.* This land is similar to 1(A) but as a result of a high permanent water table, liability to winter or occasional flooding, or somewhat heavier or less tractable soils, it is less suitable to arable cultivation than to grass. Such land may be converted into 1(A) by drainage or prevention of flooding, but this is a major operation. Designation is 3 (G).

4 *Good but Heavy Land.* Although such land has soils of good depth and the natural fertility is often high, the soils, mostly the better clays and heavy loams, are heavy, and both the period of working and the range of possible crops are restricted. Designation is 4(A).

Category II—Medium Quality Land

Land of only medium productivity even when under good management. Productivity is limited by reason of the unfavorable operation of one or more of the factors of site or soil character. Thus by reason of site: 1, high elevation; 2, steepness; 3, unfavorable aspect. By reason of soil: 1, shallowness; 2, defective water conditions. It is obvious that a wide range of conditions, indeed an al-

most endless combination of one, two, or more dele-
terious factors, is included in this major category.

5 *Medium Quality Light Land*. This is land defective
by reason of lightness and, usually, shallowness of
soil. The moderate elevation, relatively gentle slopes
and consequent aspects are all satisfactory. There
are several distinct types included within the category.

6 *Medium Quality General Purpose Farmland*. This
is land defective primarily by reason of relief: steep
slopes, elevation, varied aspect, and varied water
conditions. In consequence, soils are varied, often
deficient by reason of stoniness, shallowness, heaviness, or in other ways. When studied in detail,
such land may be resolved into a mosaic of small
tracts or patches—may be only a part of a field in
size—of land varying from group 1 to 10. Most land
of group 6 is usually equally suitable for crops or
grass, hence the designation 6(AG).

Category III—Poor Quality Land

Land of low productivity by the extreme operation of
one or more factors of site and soil. There are three
main groups of "extreme factors": extreme heaviness
and/or wetness of soil giving poor quality heavy land
or land in need of extensive drainage works; extreme
elevation and/or ruggedness and/or shallowness of soil
giving mountain moorland conditions; extreme lightness of soil with attendant drought and poverty giving
poor quality light land. Several factors may combine to
such an extent as to render the land agriculturally useless or almost so—such as shingle beaches or moving
sand dunes.

7 *Poor Quality Heavy Land.* This includes the more intractable clay lands and low-lying areas needing extensive drainage works before they can be rendered agriculturally useful. For convenience, undrained mosses or bogs have been included, though the soils they might eventually yield would not necessarily be heavy. The heavy clay lands tend to be in grass, hence the designation 7(G).

8 *Poor Quality Mountain Moorland.* The wide variety of land included in this group is apparent from the varied character of the natural or seminatural vegetation by which it is clothed. General designation 8(H) where H indicates heathland or moorland.

9 *Poor Quality Light Land.* This group includes the so-called "hungry" or overdrained lands, usually overlying coarse sands or porous gravels and hence including both coastal sand dunes and the inland sandy "wastes" or heathland. Designation is 9(H).

10 *Poorest Land.* In its present state this land may be agriculturally useless, but this is not to deny possibilities of reclamation. Salt marshes can be drained, sand dunes fixed, and so on.

The proportions of each of these types of land in the different parts of Britain are given in Table XVIII.

Need for Continuing Research

In order to conserve as far as possible for food production the land most suitable to the purpose, mobile industries and housing developments, including new towns, are to be sited, other things being equal, on the poorer lands. Thus there has been developed the concept of the *optimum use of land,* that is the optimum use of every acre in the national interest. Another con-

Table XVIII. Classification of Land in Britain

	England and Wales*		Scotland		Great Britain	
	Acres	%	Acres	%	Acres	%
Category I—Good	17,845,900	47.9	3,963,300	20.8	21,809,200	38.7
1 First class	1,963,100	5.3	396,800	2.1	2,359,900	4.2
2 Good general farm						
2(A) For plowing	7,065,600	18.9	1,735,900	9.1	8,801,500	15.6
2(AG) Crops or grass	2,636,900	7.1	192,900	1.0	2,829,800	5.0
3 First class, restricted	1,234,800	3.3	8,700	0.0	1,243,500	2.2
4 Good but heavy	4,945,500	13.3	1,629,000	8.6	6,574,500	11.7
Category II—Medium	11,933,800	32.0	2,877,400	15.1	14,811,200	26.3
5 Medium light land						
5(A) For plowing	2,402,100	6.4	77,400	0.4	2,479,500	4.4
5(G) Not for plowing	220,300	0.6	300	0.0	220,600	0.4
6 Medium general farm	9,311,400	25.0	2,779,700	14.7	12,111,100	21.5
Category III—Poor	6,350,900	17.0	12,113,800	63.5	18,464,700	32.8
7 Heavy land	825,900	2.2	54,100	0.3	880,000	1.6
8 Mountain and moor	4,516,800	12.1	12,001,700	62.9	16,518,500	29.3
9 Light land	811,800	2.2	57,900	0.3	869,700	1.5
10 Poorest land	196,400	0.5	100	0.0	196,500	0.4
Closely built over	1,142,700	3.1	114,200	0.6	1,256,900	2.2
TOTAL	37,273,300		19,068,700		56,342,000	

* Including the Isle of Man.

cept is *multiple use of land*, the making of one piece serve more than one purpose, for instance as gathering ground for water supply, afforestation, and public recreation. Then there is the elimination of waste. Old industrial sites have been redeveloped as recreational areas, playing fields, and housing sites to the general improvement of the appearance of the countryside. New Yorkers will naturally draw the comparison between the old state of some of the valleys north of the city or the collection of derelict shacks along the Hudson waterfront before the construction of New York's unmatched system of parkways.

Even in their much-studied country, workers in Britain are conscious of conspicuous gaps in knowledge. A soil survey, though begun, remains to be completed. Little is known about population trends. The structure, movements, and habits of the rural population have been insufficiently studied. And so the story goes—the need for a constant stream of research work and a team of researchers in addition to those technicians engaged in the actual work of preparing plans.

Before the war, Britain was producing roughly one-third of its food, and the submarine menace and threatened blockade brought the country face to face with the specter of starvation. Farmers of Britain made a supreme effort: the country was organized on a county basis, each county had its County War Agricultural Executive Committee, composed of local farmers, landowners, land agents, and others, with wide powers. The government, with the internal policy already mentioned, indicated to each county its share, that is its goal, in increased production. The county committees developed a pool of machinery, expert advisers, labor, seeds, manures, and other facilities to help the small man. Farmers were graded into A, good; B, medium; and C, poor. If a C farmer did not improve his grading he was liable to ejection, though this drastic step proved necessary in very few cases. Derelict land was taken in hand and farmed by the county committees. As a result of all these activities the production for many commodities was doubled and in the space of three brief years Britain was producing more than half the food consumed, and this with a decreased labor force and the substitution of 80,000 members of the Women's Land· Army for male labor. At a later stage prisoner-of-war labor was used in such work as improvement of drainage, cutting of ditches, fencing, general work of maintenance, as well as harvesting. As previously described, agriculture was almost completely mechanized. Britain's neglected agricultural industry emerged from the war a much more efficient force.

In many ways, the farming industry is still on a wartime footing. There are still county committees, reorganized on a more democratic basis, and there is still power to eliminate the C farmer. The new power to create agricultural small holdings to serve as training grounds is a ladder for those who would enter the industry. The close liaison between the scientific research stations and the working farmers established during the war has been regularized by the creation of the National Agricultural Advisory Service. Questions involving the alienation of agricultural land for other uses are the concern of the Agricultural Land Service. Where the government is compelled to take over land, either to farm it or reorganize it, there is the Agricultural Land Commission for the purpose. A close liaison is maintained with the Forestry Commission, orginally charged with the task of afforesting one and three-quarters million acres of land when it was constituted in 1918–19, and now concerned with developing forests of over 5 million acres and taking a part in the management of private woodlands. The integration of agriculture and forestry is not simple, but it is making headway.

Despite the high level of achievement of British farming indicated by acre yields and of increased output per worker (Table XII), it is the belief of experts that much more might yet be accomplished. For example, average milk yields are still low. If an overall yield from dairy herds of 800 gallons per annum per cow could be secured, milk output would be doubled. There is much marginal land in Britain, particularly on the fringes of the upland moors. An American might describe this as range country, but it is much wetter, in fact it usually suffers from an excess of moisture. Following the world-famed experiments of Sir George Stapleton, much of this land could be disk-plowed, reseeded with nutritious grasses, and could then carry a much larger stock, with a much larger home production of both beef and mutton. At the other extreme, the more intensive use of some of the best lands could result in a high production of vegetables and fruits.

But other problems, of course, are involved, Britain's international commitments, for instance. Already difficulties have been created through one ministry importing foreign fruit and vegetables at a time when unexpectedly large British crops came on the market. There is the ever-present question of costs: how far the subsidies, running at a high level, should be and can be maintained. Increasing expenses in overseas countries have produced a position, rare before World War II, when British costs of production at present rates of exchange are little if at all above those in the countries from whom her imports are received. It has, for example, been stated that even the cost of production of a bushel of British wheat is now as low as that of any of the chief wheat-producing countries, though Britain with its well-distributed and on the whole heavy rainfall is not suited, except in the eastern counties, for cereal production.

One point remains to be stressed. Britain and other countries, especially those of northwest Europe, have evolved a well-balanced, mixed agriculture, based essentially on rotation of crops and on the coordination of arable farming with stock rearing and feeding. This is a type of farming that not only preserves the qualities of the soil, but is designed to improve its nutrient status and texture. By and large the better British farmer is the tenant farmer. When he has paid his modest rent

to the generally impoverished landlord, the remainder
of his liquid assets can be used to improve his standard
of farming, and in many cases tenant farmers remain
on their holdings for thirty, forty, fifty or more years.
The owner-occupier, on the other hand, is too often
short of capital to run his holding properly. The traditional social organization of British farming into landlord, tenant-farmer, and farm worker is firmly established and normally successful.

It may be said that the trend of the world as a whole
is rather toward the British model than away from it.
In this connection arises the disputed question of the
size of the holding. The average British full-time
farmer, as shown by the 1941 Farm Survey (p. 108), has
just under 100 acres of improved land, that is of crops
and grass. On really good land the holdings are smaller,
on poorer land they are larger, and on marginal land
ten acres of rough grazing, unenclosed, is reckoned as
equivalent to one acre of enclosed, improved grazing.
This has been the average-size holding for at least a
hundred years. Farms show little tendency to consoli-
date; indeed there are fewer large farms than fifty years
ago. Small holdings are sometimes consolidated but this
is offset by the break-up of other units for new small
holdings. It may be that the farm of 100 acres is not the
ideal economic size, but it has become the standard
unit, provided with a farmstead and farm buildings of
a permanent character. In the United States, too, there
seems to be a general trend toward a family farm of
comparable size. British farmers, like farmers the world

over, are marked by a sturdy independence, and coop-
erative enterprise has not proved easy to establish. A
promising line of development whereby a holding com-
pany holds a number of farms, each under a manager,
has proved successful in some cases, but it is a type of
organization still rare.

Closely bound up with the established holding of 100
or 120 acres is the fact that it can be divided into 10 or
12 fields of 10 acres each. Ten acres is large enough
for mechanized cultivation with the small machines
adapted to European conditions, but it is also small
enough for controlled grazing, so important for the adequate use of grass. A holding of this size is "flexible."
It can be worked as an all-arable farm on a three-course
or a four-course rotation; on the Scottish system of
three years crops, three years grass; as well as on the
long-ley system of, say, nine years grass and three years
crops. It can, of course, also be an all-grass holding, and
this flexibility has proved of the greatest advantage under wartime conditions, when the former all-grass holdings were once more subject to plowing. It is perhaps
desirable to stress again at this point the enormously
important part which has always been played in British
farming by the careful management of permanent grass.
Permanent grass is not, as it is in so many countries, an
indication of land unfit for plowing.

The adaptation of European practice to modern conditions of farming demands new farm implements; but
not of the types designed for the monoculture of the new

lands, not the 18- and 24-foot-cut combine-harvesters, for instance, but a whole range of machines designed for the particular conditions involved. I repeat unequivocally that agricultural machinery designed for American conditions is by and large unsuitable for the Old World and the rehabilitation of the war-devastated lands of Europe.

INDIA AND PAKISTAN

The burden of this chapter is that the salvaging of the Old World lies in part in increasing agricultural efficiency and output. So far we have limited ourselves to Europe. We shall now take India and Pakistan to illustrate a phase of the problem widely applicable to the rest of the Old World. India and Pakistan are primarily self-supporting but at a low level. It is perhaps a little surprising to find that, despite the enormous population of India and Pakistan, land per capita works out at 2.6 acres. Mountains, deserts, poor soil, reduce this crude figure, as the analysis in Table XIX shows. A notable feature of the table is the large area classed as "cultivable waste." Much of this is rough grazing, often common to the village, where mixed herds of goats and sheep do more than graze—they successfully eradicate almost every living thing, stirring up the clouds of dust inevitably associated with rural India in the dry season and paving the way for soil erosion when the rains come.

There are large areas, too, of what in Africa would

TABLE XIX. LAND USE IN PART OF INDIA AND PAKISTAN*

	India		Pakistan		Total	
	Acres	%	Acres	%	Acres	%
Net area sown	170,808,000	42.5	46,277,000	42.2	217,085,000	42.4
Current fallows	37,937,000	9.4	8,906,000	8.1	46,843,000	9.1
Cultivable waste	68,556,000	17.1	21,159,000	19.3	89,715,000	17.6
Not available for cultivation	62,413,000	15.5	27,930,000	25.5	90,343,000	17.7
Forests	62,491,000	15.5	5,335,000	4.9	67,826,000	13.2
TOTAL	402,205,000		109,607,000		511,812,000	

* Table from O. H. K. Spate *in* L. D. Stamp: *Asia*, 8th ed., Dutton, 1950. Values are recalculated from 1945–46 figures for the old provinces of British India only, i.e. excluding the former Native States. Estimated population of the above area 300,000,000, representing 1.7 acres per head (total); 0.7 acres cropped. The area included is about half that of the total of India and Pakistan, i.e. 1,011,200,000 acres; with a population (1941) of 389,000,000, a density of 246 a square mile or 2.6 acres a head.

be called open savanna, or thorn forest. These are un-cultivated for reasons of poverty of soil, existence of hardpan, unreliability of rainfall or water supply, and the many other factors that impede the development of tropical regions. Other areas remain uncultivated be-cause of their liability to flood, though every visitor to India knows how well used are some of the banks of alluvium left uncovered in the beds or along the banks of rivers in the low-water season.

The actual cultivated area of India is only about 0.7 or 0.75 acres per head of population. Comparatively speaking, this is not a desperately small amount, but here it is combined with very low yields. Approximately 77 per cent of the crop acreage (1941) is devoted to food grains, with rice in the lead (26 per cent) followed by millets (20 per cent) and wheat (9 per cent); oil seeds and cotton each occupy about 7 per cent.

In India agricultural production remains at a relatively inefficient level because of the vicious circle in which the cultivator is entoiled. He is poor; therefore he cannot buy efficient implements or fertilizer; he plants his seed laboriously by hand on land which he has scratched with his oxplow. He himself, his family, and his animals are undernourished, lacking energy for hard work. Because he cannot afford to buy fuel for cooking he burns the dung of his cattle, the only available material, thereby robbing the land even of animal manure. Consequently his crop yields are low, he needs nearly all his produce to feed his family and his few poor animals, and he has no surplus for sale. Because he has no surplus for sale he remains poor, and his poverty is increased by his usual indebtedness to the money lender and to the incidence of such heavy expenses as providing marriage dowries for his daughters.

The problem is how to break this vicious circle. If the millions of cultivators could be *given* fertilizers, and better implements and seed, and instructed in their proper use, they would get better crops with a better yield, build up their own strength and that of their families and their animals and have a surplus for sale—unless the net result of increased production would merely mean the increase of the family and a still larger number of mouths to feed. Otherwise we might go on with the story, see a surplus of produce, of sales to the towns, and increased money income, and, presuming a wise expenditure, an all-round raising of the standard of living. It is well, however, to stress that nothing would be gained at this stage by any change in agricultural production that resulted in saving of manpower. That would simply throw the entire rural economy of the country out of gear. It may even be doubted whether there is room for the gas or oil-burning machine which would rob the cultivator of his bullocks and the manure that they yield. India might better use some of the smaller specialized types of farm implements rather than attempt large-scale farm mechanization.

THE COLOMBO PLAN

When India and Pakistan became independent in 1947 and elected to remain members of the British Commonwealth of Nations and when Ceylon, in February, 1948, became the youngest self-governing Dominion, a new era of cooperation became possible in southeast Asia. In January, 1950, Colombo, capital of Ceylon, acted as host to a conference of Commonwealth prime ministers, and at that conference the Commonwealth Consultative Committee was established. It met later in the year with representatives from the governments of Australia, Canada, Ceylon, India, New Zealand, Pakistan, and the United Kingdom and with delegates or observers from Burma, Siam, Indochina, and Indonesia. The Colombo Plan embraces all south and southeast Asia, an area with a quarter of the whole population of the world. The Plan, as drawn up and published, reviews the problems of the whole area with special reference to the aspects of war and the comparative levels of economic development and outlines development programs for each main area.

In 1957 the program, if completed, in India, Pakistan, Ceylon, Malaya, and British Borneo would result
in an increase of 3.5 per cent in land under cultivation
(13 million acres), 17 per cent more under irrigation,
10 per cent increase in production of food grains, and
67 per cent in electric generating capacity. The estimated cost of the scheme (1951–57) is £1,868 million,
of which £1,084 million or about $3,035 million would
be needed from external sources. Special emphasis is
placed upon the trained personnel needed, and details
are given of each main item of expenditure. The Plan
is a realistic challenge to a large part of the Old World
to face its many problems squarely.

NATIONAL AND INTERNATIONAL ASPECTS

It seems clear that in attempting to work out their
salvation the densely populated countries of the Old
World must adopt some scheme whereby each prepares
in advance for the use of its land. How far, it may
be asked, is such national land planning compatible
with international aspects? On the one hand we can
take the point of view that the world has become a single unit and that there should be universal free trade,
free exchange of goods, and an unfettered distribution
of products. One may postulate the ideal world in
which there is an equal standard of living in every
country, in which every part of the world produces
those commodities for which it is best fitted by its
natural resources, that when one part becomes overpopulated the population moves freely to another part,

and so on. We have all of us heard condemned the wickedness of some countries which burn their surplus coffee or throw it into the sea, of countries which burn their wheat surplus, or slaughter their pigs, or throw fish on the farms as manure, or burn their surplus raisins—but it is difficult to suggest simply a free distribution of the world's wealth among the world's poor relations. As in the experience of almost any individual human family, the poor relations may be more or less, probably less, grateful; but gratitude is not likely to mend their ways.

Surely it is better to take the realistic view, so well expressed some time ago by Professor J. D. Black of Harvard: [2] "Considerable food does move from one country to another but the adjustment of population to resources is still largely a matter for each country by itself . . . each country must work out a solution for itself." Surely it is up to every country in the world to practice the good old virtue of thrift, and to do the utmost to develop home resources, which, in the case of the countries of the Old World, involves a carefully planned use of land.

CHAPTER VII

Preserving the New World

IT IS not so long since the phrase "Go west, young man" summed up the North American attitude towards the obvious direction of advancement. Going west dates essentially from the opening up of the lines of communication across the Appalachian barrier. The completion of the Erie canal in 1824, giving direct water communication between New York and the Great Lakes, established the era of rapid western movement of settlement; and the railway in due course replaced the covered wagon as the pioneers' main form of transportation.

THE PIONEER FRINGE

At first the West seemed limitless—the apparently in-exhaustible stretches of prairie just waiting to be marked out in 160-acre blocks, the deep, fertile, easily worked soils just waiting for the first touch of the plow to be changed into the greatest cornlands and wheat-lands the world had ever known. Those who traveled ever farther and farther west did not at first appreciate that with a lower rainfall came also the greater uncertainty of that rainfall and the consequent danger of periodic crop failures.

So we reach the pioneer fringe, where nature and man are engaged in a never-ending struggle for supremacy, man on his side seeking to push the limits of cultivation farther and farther into the semiarid lands, nature by exhibiting her vagaries from year to year encouraging the bold pioneer in one season, heartlessly breaking him the next. As Isaiah Bowman's famous study on *The Pioneer Fringe* demonstrated, and as others have so fully endorsed since, there are large areas where nature has won, where settlements have been abandoned, and where the fields laboriously carved out have once again reverted to their natural state. Such pioneer fringes are found all over the world. Everywhere are signs both of man's successes and of his failures. It is sometimes said that in this day and age the pioneer spirit is dead. It is truer to say that in the struggle with nature man has had to reorganize his campaign on a different basis. In clearing tropical forest and thorn scrub he may need to use the heaviest machinery yet designed. In attempting to make his ventures pay, he may have to use the largest scale farm implements.

Today's pioneer must be backed with abundant capital resources, and this means an attack, not by an individual but by a group, in many, perhaps the majority of cases, by state enterprise. Two things stand out clearly: first, that pioneering in the new sense is by no means dead; second, that there are few if any easily conquerable areas left. The final outcome of the assault on these areas, notably in the tropics, has not yet been decided by any manner of means. Those who complacently refer to the "vast underdeveloped areas of the world," speaking as if their potential resources were already developed, overlook the fact that the battle is not yet won, indeed that we do not yet know how the battle should be fought.

MISTAKES OF THE PIONEERS

The pioneers of old made many mistakes. The pioneers of today are still making mistakes—with this difference, that today's mistakes are much bigger or affect larger areas and greater issues.

The individual pioneers of old were equipped with knowledge derived from their own personal experience in their homelands. The Pilgrim Fathers who came to New England from old England brought with them agricultural implements, techniques, crops and animals, building and house styles, and further, they brought with them their own concept of the good life. They suffered severely in the early years before they adapted their *modus operandi* to the severe winters and the hotter summers of a land naturally less fertile than the one they had left. Everywhere in New England we see abandoned fields covered with second-growth forest, representing the virgin land cleared at great cost of labor by those intrepid settlers, little knowing that they were expending their energy on land too poor ever to return a due reward for their toil.

The world is full of examples of the mistakes of the pioneers. Among old and long-forgotten books on the theme is Sir Samuel W. Baker's *Eight Years in Ceylon,* to which reference has already been made. Sir Samuel, believing that the life of the country gentleman in mid-nineteenth-century England would never be again what it had been before, decided to establish himself in Ceylon. He took with him his carriage, his coachman and his horses; his bailiff, his cowman, bull and cow and rams; his seed oats and his seed wheat; and last but not least, a pack of foxhounds and a greyhound. He saw the jungle-covered, grassy plains among the hills of Ceylon destined by nature to become a country gentleman's estate on the English model. The story, of course, tells how his crops failed—not one of the English introductions did he succeed in establishing in his new island home—and how his cattle and horses died. His heavy coach was wrecked, but the coachman, not to be outdone, pressed an elephant into service and gained the reputation of being the only man ever to drive an elephant to death by trying to make it gallop!

Fantastic as this story sounds, the pioneers of the present day are doing precisely the same kind of thing. Sir Samuel "purchased farming implements of the most improved descriptions." We are at this very moment using machinery designed for the prairies of Canada on experimental farms in tropical Africa and knowing almost as little about the fundamental factors of climate and the effect on soil formation and plant growth. The pioneers of old made mistakes, oft times to ruination not only of themselves but to the land where they tried to settle. The great danger today is that we may be doing damage a hundred times more serious than that wrought by the individual pioneer in the past. There is in fact one result of our activity rightly described as the greatest scourge the world has ever known—I refer, of course, to soil erosion. G. V. Jacks and R. O. Whyte's *The Rape of the Earth* (American title *Vanishing Lands*), 1939, was the first serious world survey of its evils. Many others have followed and we are now in the difficult position of having to assess what is real and what is exaggerated in the many semi-popular books and articles on the subject.

Soil Erosion

Every geologist is familiar with the erosion cycle. No sooner has an area of land been raised above sea level than it becomes subject to the erosive forces of nature. The rain beats down on the ground and washes away the finer particles, sweeping them into rivulets and then into rivers and out to sea. The frost freezes the rain water in cracks of the rocks and breaks up even the hardest of the constituents of the earth's crust. Blocks of rock dislodged at high levels are brought down by the force of gravity. Alternate heating and cooling of bare rock surfaces causes their disintegration. In the arid regions of the world the wind is a powerful force in removing material from one area to another. All this is natural. But nature has also provided certain defensive forces. Bare rock surfaces are in due course protected by soil, itself dependent initially on the weathering of the rocks. Slowly but surely, different types of soil with differing "profiles" evolve, the main types depending primarily on the climate. The protective soil covering, once it is formed, is held together by the growth of vegetation. Grass and herbaceous plants, with long, branching, tenuous roots, hold firmly together the surface particles. The same is true with the forest cover. The heaviest tropical downpours beating on the leaves of the giant trees reach the ground only as spray, gently watering the surface layers and penetrating along the long passages provided by the roots to the lower levels of the soil. The soil, thus protected by grass, herbs, or trees, furnishes a quiet habitat for a myriad varied organisms; earthworms that importantly modify the soil; bacteria, active in their work of converting fallen leaves and decaying vegetation into humus and food for the growing plants. Chemical action is constantly taking place; soil acids attack mineral particles, and salts in solution move from one layer in the soil to another.

We may sum this up by saying that under the natural vegetative cover, the soil profile proper to the climatic conditions and the parent rock substances gradually develops. It is a long process, and in many areas there has not been sufficient time, in the geological sense, for completion of the process; the soils are "immature."

Now let us consider what happens when man, the pioneer, comes along. He plows up the natural grasslands. He removes the numerous branching roots that have held together the surface particles, now easily moved by the action of rain and wind. In plowing he has mixed together the surface layers and provided his crops with a medium in which they can grow and develop and in which natural plant food is present in varying degree or which may be supplemented by animal or chemical manures. But he has also exposed the soil to the action of the atmosphere. In some parts of the world exposure is useful: in a cold climate the breaking up of the clods of clay by frost action is beneficial. At the other extreme, as we have already pointed out, in tropical climates, by exposure to the atmosphere such rapid chemical action may have been set up that the natural plant food in the soil is quickly destroyed.

Broadly speaking the position is worst when the natural vegetation is forest. Not only does man, the pioneer, rob the soil of its source of humus, the fallen leaves, but he exposes a soil quite unused to the direct rays of the sun and the direct fall of the rain to the immediate influence of both. For example, much of the upland and west coast of Scotland was once forested with the beautiful Scots fir (*Pinus sylvestris*). The heavy rain, falling on the close pine woods, trickled gradually to the ground and soaked into the soil. Much was evaporated from the leaves, and the floor of the forest, covered with pine needles, remained comparatively dry, supporting a sparse cover or undergrowth of various shade-loving plants or low shrubs such as bilberry and heather. When the forests were cut down, the heavy rain fell straight onto the surface soil more rapidly than it could drain away. Especially where there was no steep slope the water was held up, and moisture-loving plants began to flourish, particularly sphagnum, or bog moss. Once the sphagnum was established it acted as a sponge. True, it prevented soil erosion, but it grew and grew until great thicknesses of moss blanketed the whole countryside. Thus huge stretches of bog land, that known to the botanists as "blanket bog," extending over wide areas of Scotland and Ireland, are directly due to man's action.[1]

A different, perhaps more familiar, example is seen in many of the hilly parts of the Southern states. The originally forested slopes were cleared by the pioneers for timber or for the creation of farmlands. The bare soil was left unprotected; heavy downpours of rain rapidly washed it away and one gets the familiar feature of gully erosion and of hillsides literally swept bare of any vestige of soil. But of course this example could be multiplied elsewhere in the United States and all over the world. No more heart-breaking story of man's improvidence is told than in the barren, eroded hills of China, land of famine.

Now what is the present situation in the United States? Dr. Hugh H. Bennett supplies the following estimate from the Soil Conservation Service of the Department of Agriculture (1934 survey, supplemented by more recent detailed surveys): land no longer used for cultivated crops, except in small, scattered areas, owing to severe erosion, 100 million acres; total area of crop and grazing land seriously affected by erosion, 282 million acres; land moderately affected by erosion, 775 million acres.

When one bears in mind that the greater part of the area to which these figures refer has been settled only some 100 years or less, we get a glimpse of the incredible destruction that can be caused by uncontrolled soil erosion. Only slowly are the nations of the world becoming aware of the gravity of a situation in which the world bids fair to starve itself to death by its stupid behavior, through a process which has been well called "the mining" of the soil for the sake of "cheap" food. On many occasions I have quoted from my experiences when studying the soil erosion problem in West Africa, where it is an ever-present danger. Soil erosion has been noticeably increased where knowledge of the control of animal diseases has increased the size of the herds and resulted in overgrazing. Unhappily, I can say in all truth that the worst soil erosion that I saw in West Africa was on a government experimental farm! It illustrates only too well the danger of taking our mid-latitude experience and thinking that it will apply to other different conditions, such as those found in the tropics.

CONTROL OF SOIL EROSION

In this section I do not propose to deal with the beneficial results of contour plowing, with the effects of strip cropping, or with the different methods of blocking gulleys and establishing vegetation cover to prevent the spread of soil erosion. These matters are familiar, or should be, and are dealt with at length in many technical reports and well-known books. Rather am I concerned that there should be an understanding of the numerous effective ways in which native peoples throughout the world have recognized the dangers and the evils of soil erosion and have developed their own ways of counteracting it. We are apt to be so obsessed with our own superior knowledge that we are unwilling to learn from those whom we regard as our inferiors. Admittedly there are parts of the world where the native peoples know little of the arts of cultivation; but also, there are lands where native cultivators have a good deal to teach us.

In the wetter parts of West Africa, "basin" cultivation is widely practiced. Let us look at the operation in a little more detail.[2] In the first place, the forest is cleared over small areas only, so that if erosion does attack a field, its incidence is limited. There is no clear felling over large tracts. When the small area to be cultivated is selected, the soil is carefully hoed up by hand into a series of ridges, and the furrows between are crossed at intervals, say six to ten feet, by transverse ridges. If a very heavy downpour of rain occurs, some of the soil will be washed from the ridges, but it will not go farther than into the little basins containing the water. Incidentally, under such an arrangement it is possible to grow two types of crops, one moisture-loving and one which prefers a better-drained soil on the ridges. This system of peasant cultivation is laborious in the extreme, but we may recall that the principle was considered as a solution of soil erosion problems in the United States, and that a special type of plow, the "basin lister," was designed to create similar little basins by mechanical means.

Let us take another instance from West Africa. The European or North American visitor to the Gold Coast may find it difficult to know when he is on the cultivated part of a native farm and when he is in the surrounding jungle. The whole seems to him to be a tangle of weeds and of odd trees, and he longs to teach the peasant the virtues of a clean farm and of weed control. But in fact the weeds act as a protection to the soil, and replacement of the "dirty" Gold Coast farm by a clean-swept European model would quickly result in loss of soil and soil fertility. Clearly the object here should be to develop the system by substituting a cover crop of value in itself for useless weeds.

For another example we may turn to the Peruvian Andes and the ancient system of terracing, the *andenes,* that made productive steep slopes where no modern system of cultivation could hope to succeed. We know, too, how, from the point of view of land conservation, the shifting cultivation common in much of tropical America is wasteful of land and gives but small returns, but is conservative of both the soil and soil fertility.

Reference has been made above (p. 147) to the poverty of much of Italy's land. Here again, in the dry Mediterranean climate, are careful terracing and the conservation of the little bits of soil, often laboriously gathered together to make fields where none existed before. Even more remarkable is what happens in parts of central China, where a farmer, having land with one type of soil, say heavy clay, will exchange so many thousand basketfuls with another farmer whose land is too light and sandy. In our modern view perhaps this may sound ridiculous, but experiments are now taking place in eastern England where on light glacial sands, clay is being spread by giant bulldozers to create a fertile loam where only a hungry sand existed before.

I consider it of fundamental importance that we study intensively all native systems of cultivation before we condemn them. There is so often an element of knowledge in local practices that might well be adapted to modern systems for developing the underdeveloped lands. Native "superstition" gave the world both quinine and cocaine. There is often even a hidden scientific meaning behind native superstitions.

A WORLD LAND USE SURVEY

Whatever part of the world we consider, there are always reasons, whether of natural factors of relief, soil, and climate or the consequence of man's occupancy, that have determined its use, past and present, even if only in a negative sense. Surely it is of the utmost importance to determine the present usage and to ascertain, if possible, how it came into being. For any further development must start from the present. In a number of countries this need has been recognized and land-use surveys have been carried out. I have already given details of the work which has been done in Britain and I shall not attempt to summarize the many surveys which have been carried out in the United States, Canada, Australia, and elsewhere. I would, however, mention one thing, and that is the danger of confusing two issues. To make a survey of existing land use is primarily objective. To seek for the factors which are operative is a scientific search for truth. As soon as we begin to think in terms of potential use, what land ought to be used for, we are introducing a subjective element. In due course planning of land use in this way may be of the utmost importance, but it is fundamental that the two stages, for such they are, should not be confused.

In view of the increasingly urgent problem of feeding the world, a world land-use inventory or survey had been proposed. It was taken up at the International Geographical Congress in Lisbon, April, 1949. UNESCO gave its support and a commission of four met at Clark University, Worcester, Mass., in December, 1949, and drew up a unanimous report on objectives and procedure.[3] The following are abstracts from its report.

It was pointed out that many countries have collected statistics of land use and agriculture, sometimes in very considerable detail, but that it is only by recording the facts on maps that actual distributions can be shown. This is where the work of the proposed World Land Use Survey would be fundamental and unique. It is proposed that the Survey should be carried out on the best maps available to the country concerned, but that pub-

lication should be on the uniform scale of 1 : 1,000,000,
and that each map should be accompanied by an explanatory memorandum or memoir. The commission is
fully aware that the explanatory memoirs can give only
partial answers to the many problems that will be
raised, since many other parallel investigations are
needed, such as soil surveys, ecological surveys, climato-
logical and demographic studies. The report underlines
what has been said above when it states that "unless the
present use of land is known and understood, development schemes may cut across the existing economic
structure in such a way as to cause more harm than
good."

In view of the fact that already comparable work had
been initiated by the Pan American Institute of Historical and Geographical Studies covering the Americas,
an office was established on January 1, 1951, at the
Royal Geographical Society in London to undertake
pilot surveys or coordinate work in different parts of the
Old World. It is hoped that it will later be possible to
establish a World Land-Use Survey with permanent
headquarters to correlate work carried out by partici-
pating countries all over the world or by detailing
groups of trained personnel to conduct the surveys. It
is suggested that a simple master key, with subdivisions
according to local needs, be adopted for the whole
world. These categories are explained in the commission's report and some of the salient points are noted
below.

SCHEME OF CLASSIFICATION FOR THE
WORLD LAND-USE SURVEY

1 Settlements and associated nonagricultural lands
2 Horticulture
3 Tree and other perennial crops
4 Cropland
     (a) Continual and rotation cropping
     (b) Land rotation
5 Improved permanent pasture (managed or enclosed)
6 Unimproved grazing land
     (a) Used
     (b) Not used
7 Woodlands
     (a) Dense
     (b) Open
     (c) Scrub
     (d) Swamp forests
     (e) Cut-over or burnt-over forest areas
     (f) Forest with subsidiary cultivation
8 Swamps and Marshes (fresh- and salt-water, non-forested)
9 Unproductive land

1. *Settlements and associated nonagricultural lands.* On the million scale it is recognized that it will only be possible to indicate the larger cities and towns.

2. *Horticulture.* This category is intended to include all intensive cultivation of vegetables and small fruits, as distinct from tree fruits—such as truck farming in America and market gardening in England and other European countries, as well as the production from larger gardens and allotments whether the crops are

grown for sale or not, including for instance, the garden cultivation of tropical villages, as in Malaya.

3. *Tree and other perennial crops.* The wide range
included in this category covers numerous tropical
plantations and the orchards of mid-latitudes.

4. *Cropland* is divided into (a) continual and rotation cropping and (b) land rotation. Continual crops
are indicated as meaning, for example, rice, which is
often the only crop grown year after year on the same
land, and also sugar cane and such monocultural crops
as wheat and corn. By rotation crops is understood those
grown in a fixed or variable rotation, including fodder
grass, clover, and alfalfa, which may occupy land for two
or three years. Land rotation is the category covering
the system whereby cultivation is carried out for a few
years and the land then allowed to rest for a considerable period before the scrub or coarse grass is again
cleared and the land recultivated. Since this category
will cover a very large proportion of the territory in the
underdeveloped countries, its mapping is clearly of the
utmost importance. The careless observer is too often
misled by what appears to be scrub or second growth
forest and fails to appreciate that it is land being rested
in a regular system of land rotation.

5. *Improved permanent pasture* (managed or enclosed). This is a type of land-use well understood in
countries like New Zealand and Britain, where controlled grazing is carried on in small enclosed fields, the
grass being managed by manuring, by liming, sometimes by reseeding, or in other ways. Often the grasses,
including clovers, have been introduced so that the pasture is not "natural." Some land of this sort is grazed;
some is cut for hay or dried grass. In other countries,
such as the United States, this category of land is less

distinctive, but it would include the intensively stocked grasslands of the dairy belts.

6. *Unimproved grazing land: (a) used, (b) not used*. This may be described as extensive pasture or range land. It may be enclosed in large units but is not as a rule in small fields. It is not fertilized or deliberately manured though it may be periodically burned over. The vegetation is that native to the locality, although its characteristics often have been modified by grazing or occasionally by the introduction of non-local plants. A great range of vegetation is included, from tropical savanna to arctic tundra, and as far as possible the type of vegetation should be described on the map or accompanying notes. For example, this category will include savanna, tropical grassland (e.g. llanos), steppe land, dry pampas, and short-grass prairie. The category will also include such range lands as bunch grass and sage brush and creosote bush, as well as the vegetation of the High Veld and the Karroo of South Africa. It will include the heather moorlands and heathlands and grass moorlands of Europe. It is clear that care must be taken to distinguish these very varied types.

There are many areas of such land which at present are not used in different parts of the world, though they differ but little from those which are used for grazing.

7. *Woodlands*. Forest and woodland differ greatly from one part of the world to another. The main categories suggested refer to the morphological character of the forest, independently of the age of the trees: (a) Dense, where the crowns of the trees are touching; (b) Open, where the crowns of the trees do not touch and the land between is occupied by grass or other ground vegetation. Where trees are sparse such land comes into Category 6 (grazing land); (c) Scrub, designating vege-

tation such as the maquis of Europe, chaparral of North America, mallee and mulga of Australia, and the acacia-thorn scrub of Africa and India; (d) Swamp forests, both fresh-water and tidal; (e) Cut-over or burnt-over forest areas not yet fully reclothed; (f) Forest with subsidiary cultivation, comprising: (1) Shifting cultivation, where patches of land are cleared for cultivation from time to time, usually, but not always, by wandering tribes; (2) Forest-crop economy. Such is the system, for example, in parts of eastern Canada, where holdings consist mainly of woodland but where some cultivation is carried on subsidiary to the working and management by replanting of the forest land.

8. *Swamps and Marshes (fresh- and salt-water, non-forested.)*

9. *Unproductive land.* A great variety of land is also included in this category. Much appears bare, and though it may support lowly forms of plant life, it is essentially unproductive. Barren mountains, rocky and sandy deserts, moving sand dunes, salt flats, and ice fields are examples.

LINES OF DEVELOPMENT

Much of the development that has been taking place over the past century has been in the so-called "new lands," especially of the Western Hemisphere. This has resulted in wholesale destruction: forests have been recklessly cleared and cutover lands neither replanted nor utilized for food production; grasslands have been ruthlessly plowed, the soil mined and the land abandoned to the ravages of soil erosion; range lands have been so heavily stocked that the native vegetation has been destroyed. In other areas of the world native economies have been so upset by contact with Western ideas that they no longer function and settlements are abandoned. There also are areas, smaller but extensive in the aggregate, where mining operations have laid waste the land, where streams have been poisoned by noxious effluents, where nothing is left but a scene of desolation. It is little wonder that we have books with such titles as *Deserts on the March,* man-made deserts essentially, or *Vanishing Lands,* where man is responsible for the vanishing. Our urgent duty is to preserve what remains of the new lands, to start a process of rebuilding, redevelopment, and to learn the all-important lessons before undertaking extensive changes in the so-called underdeveloped lands.

Bearing all these facts in mind we may indicate some of the lines of development indicated by science. I put first and foremost the control of soil erosion and the prevention of its further spread. We have the duty of protecting the eroded valley sides by developing a natural grass cover and of protecting the steeper slopes by reforestation. On farmlands the adoption of such methods as contour plowing and strip cropping should be regarded as only a beginning of the task of building up the soil, or improving it and rendering it more productive. To some extent this means a world-wide revolution in farming and essentially the adoption in all mid-latitudes of some system of rotating crops and of introducing mixed farming, that is to say the integration of stock with arable cultivation. It may be the rotation should be a regular one of three or four years, or a system of three years in grass and three years in crops, or it may be a longer period in grass and a short period in crops. There is a trend in world farming, particularly farming in mid-latitudes, toward the general type practiced in those countries of Europe that have been shown to have the highest acre yields in the world. There is, of course, obviously no reason why there should not be a continuous improvement in the yields per man-hour consistent with high unit-area yields. This is the double aim.

A second and extremely important line of development is in the field of pest control—pests that rob us of food both before and after harvest; that prevent the keeping of animals; that prohibit the cultivation of good crops; that make human life unbearable, or even impossible. The range is enormous. To mention first the pests which attack after harvest, it has been estimated that of crops safely garnered some ten per cent is subsequently lost by the ravages of rats, mice, beetles, and other insects, molds and other fungus diseases. Determined drives are being made in many countries with regard to the rat menace, but one remembers that in hungry India enough food to feed the sub-continent for three weeks is lost every year after harvest.

With regard to pests and diseases that affect crops before harvest, science has a huge task still before it. Effective war has been waged against a number of fungus and insect diseases by spraying, but we need only to look at the yellowed, decaying pine needles of, say, the Banff area in the Canadian Rockies to see how some insect pests can get right into the plant where they are almost unassailable. Here, happily, nature took a hand by providing the very severe winter of 1949–50 and wiping out ninety per cent of the invaders. Of the virus diseases that attack plants, some seem to be transmitted via the soil from one plant to another, so that we talk about soils becoming "tomato-sick" or "strawberry-sick" and in need of sterilization.

Of the innumerable diseases affecting cattle, those which render unusable huge areas of Africa because of the presence of the tsetse fly are only too well-known. The fly has been described as the real ruler of tropical Africa. Its bite spreads the minute blood parasites of sleeping sickness in man and similar diseases in cattle. It was as recently as December, 1948, that the new drug, antrycide, developed in the laboratories of Imperial Chemical Industries, gave fresh hope for African development.

Then there are diseases peculiar to man that prevent him from properly working the land or even occupying it at all. We have witnessed the removal of yellow fever from its former strongholds, such as Panama. We know the cause of a plague and can tackle the menace. We know the cause of malaria and methods of getting rid of mosquitoes, but land is still being abandoned in crowded Bengal or is not occupied because of this widespread disease. The terrible scrub-typhus has caused the abandonment of vast tracts of land, and, despite the relative ease with which it can be controlled, so has hookworm.[4]

We are apt to forget that many diseases, though not

fatal, are terribly debilitating. Much of the food consumed by, let us say, natives in Africa does not go toward building up their resistance or providing them
with strength for working efficiently, but in repairing
the ravages due to chronic disease. Shortly after the outbreak of World War I, the distinguished biologist, Sir
Arthur Shipley, in an interesting book entitled *The
Minor Horrors of War* dealt with the troubles caused
by fleas and lice and other plagues which those who
remember trench warfare cannot fail to recall. Science
did much to eliminate these minor horrors in World
War II, but there are many parts of the world where
life is rendered almost insufferable by plagues of biting
insects. Those of us who live in screened houses may
forget their existence until we are reminded of their
potentialities, say on a hunting expedition in the Canadian wilds. Anyone who has passed a season in the Sudd
region of the Sudan will understand why the native
herdsmen spend as much time as possible in tents over
the slow burning acrid fires of cow dung.

However, elimination of such pests is not enough.
Sometimes it leaves us with new problems because we
have upset the locally established balance of nature. Dis-
turbances may likewise be caused by introductions of
alien plants or animals, whether careless or deliberate.
How pretty the water hyacinth, how delightfully attrac-
tive in an enclosed ornamental garden pond! Who
thought that its introduction into the waters of the
Irrawaddy and the delta of the Ganges might create an
almost insuperable problem of keeping a clear naviga-

ble course? It was a good idea to introduce the fleshy, firm, almost spineless prickly pear to provide a nutritious fodder in the drier parts of tropical Australia. Who would have thought that it would have spread on to the better land and that it would have been necessary to introduce the cochineal insect to destroy the plant? Who knows what measures will have to be adopted in due course to eliminate the cochineal insect? It was not long after the introduction of the muskrat into England that canal banks began to give way—canals perhaps already choked by the introduced Canadian water weed (*Elodea*)—and rivers to escape from their bounds until the new pest was eliminated. So the story goes on and on, and we realize not only the difficulties of pest control but the dangers which still lie in the path of this method of development.

In the third place we have the all-important question of the breeding and introduction of new strains of plants and new breeds or varieties of animals, to secure higher yields of grain or milk or meat, to get varieties which will mature more quickly and enable cultivation to be spread into regions at present useless because of a short growing season. There are three stages in procedure: laboratory and experimental research with small-scale tests, dissemination of the knowledge to the public, and application on a large scale. The astounding results from the development of hybrid corn over a period of a few years in the corn belt show what can be accomplished. The spread of the soya bean and the groundnut are also indicative of vast possibilities.

A highly important aspect of such work, familiar to the geographer but often neglected, is in the concept of climatic homologues, with research carried out in one part of the world leading to improvements in other parts where climatic and other conditions are, broadly speaking, comparable. Thus the Imperial College of Tropical Agriculture, situated in the island of Trinidad, is able to serve the needs of tropical lands and equatorial lands generally, both by the training of personnel and in the carrying out of research projects. The experiments which have resulted in the development of quickly maturing strains of wheat in the northern parts of the Canadian prairies are of direct and immediate interest to the Russians, who have similar lands awaiting development. The hybrid strains of rye and wheat developed in Finland are likewise of direct interest to Canada and Alaska. There are some staggering possibilities. The Russians claim to have crossed wheat with the perennial grass *Andropogon,* with the vision of a permanent grass cover, resisting soil erosion, yielding crops of wheat year after year.

In the fourth place the increasing use of fertilizers, both organic manures and chemical fertilizers, results in increasing yields. A large proportion of soils are deficient in one or another of the plant foods, and the demand for fertilizers is such that a strain has already been placed on world resources of phosphates and potash; the nitrogen of the atmosphere, however, is an inexhaustible source of nitrogenous compounds. The urban worker in the chemical factory thus is directly helping the food producer in the country. This is not the place to enter into the vexed question of natural versus artificial fertilizers. But insofar as the soil is something more than a mixture of mineral particles and has a structure resulting from the activities of soil organisms, it is logical to maintain that structure by the addition of organic matter. The well-known power of certain solutions of chemical salts to cause flocculation of clay particles would indicate that chemical compounds have the power of altering, for better or worse, the structure of a soil. Feeding the soil with plant foods is not a simple problem; bound up with it is the whole science of soil management, a field in which very little is known insofar as the tropics are concerned. The function of trace elements [5] is only beginning to be appreciated.

A fifth field of progress lies in the design and manufacture of agricultural machinery. Perhaps the world over the last century has been dominated by the concept of the machine as a means of reducing human labor, of lowering costs, or increasing production per man-hour—regardless of its after effects. Farm machinery has been designed on the get-rich-quick principle. If my contention is right, that the whole world is trending and must trend toward a balanced, mixed farming, in which field units will be small, then machinery must be redesigned to suit these conditions of good land management and not the other way round, whereby farmlands are altered to accommodate huge machines. This applies particularly to the introduction of machines into the underdeveloped tropical lands.

The processing of food products offers large opportunities. The chilling of meat revolutionized the whole of the world's meat industry. Almost as marked a revolution has been consequent on the discovery of deep freezing, still in the course of being extended. There still is an enormous waste in agricultural products, particularly in green vegetables and fruits. Something is wrong in a world which destroys a crop in one country while starvation is rampant in another. Instead of creating stockpiles for international use we live largely from hand to mouth. The world as a whole has not yet learned to follow Joseph's advice to Pharaoh.

In yet another sphere of improvement we may perhaps look for help from the sociologists and anthropologists. Man, especially primitive man, is inherently conservative. Beside the social customs to which we have previously referred which prevent limitation of families, we have such obstacles to progress as the common African concept of the value of cattle. Wealth reckoned in terms of head of cattle, independent of character, quality, or use, results in overstocking of grazing lands, with scant production of that invaluable food, milk.

Food habits often are deeply ingrained, as we know from the curiously fixed custom of the English, who demand tea, and the Americans who demand coffee—not of the English variety! As I remarked earlier, it is often said that native races in the underdeveloped lands "enjoy" a monotonous diet; but when opportunity offers greater variety they are, in fact, only too ready to forego the so-called "enjoyment."

Among the world's habits or customs which might well be abolished is the keeping of goats. It is probably true that the goat is the most destructive animal nature ever evolved. The fact that it can be kept on the poorest vegetation and at least yields something in the way of milk and meat is offset by its destructiveness. The clash between the Jewish settlers in Israel and the Arab nomads is not unconnected with the habits of the goat, which though condemned normally to live on poor grazing seizes every opportunity of trespassing on cultivated lands. From the keeping of goats one is led to inquire whether nomadism in general is not now undesirable, a practice to be gradually eliminated. Must not progress in many of the underdeveloped lands depend on the herdsman becoming a settled, mixed farmer?

These and other aspects of "World Population and World Food Supplies" were discussed by Sir John Russell in his presidential address to the British Association for the Advancement of Science in 1949. Inevitably he makes reference to Sir William Crookes's famous address of 1898 predicting a hungry world by the nineteen thirties unless yields were raised, but showing at the same time how nitrogenous fertilizers prepared synthetically from the nitrogen of the air could (as they have) save the situation. Sir John emphasizes the possibilities of the so-called marginal lands by the development of new drought-resistant grasses and leguminous fodder crops. He stresses the survey approach—the ecological view that each type of natural vegetation requires its own type of management. He examines the problems of deficiencies in little-known trace elements and the development of special modifications of such implements as the disk-plow that may bring into production vast tracts, almost unused today, of such lands as tropical Australia. And how rightly he says: "Africa's problems are fundamentally different. The small native peasant is already in occupation with his own traditional ways of life. . . . The problem is to replace his primitive methods by modern efficient methods without too great disturbance of the best elements in the native life." So "close supervision by advanced white people will be essential until Africa has its own highly efficient Universities, research workers and chemical and engineering industries." Against these potential gains Sir John sets the serious losses which may still result from soil erosion "now recognized as coming about through wrong use of land," which must be viewed both as a technical and an administrative problem. He expresses the view that I have tried to stress: "the most hopeful way of increasing world food supplies is by more intensive cultivation of the land already in use."

Sir John suggests that the three present limitations to food production, "utilisation of 7 to 10 per cent. of the earth's surface; conversion by the animal of 10 to 25 per cent. only of its food into human food; and fixation by the plant of no more than 5 per cent. of the radiant energy it receives" all are challenges to science. He concludes: "The increased food production that may confidently be expected is more than ample for population increase at Western rates. But it could easily be outstripped locally where Eastern rates of increase prevail." Unfortunately what is here meant by "Western rates" probably applies to not more than 10 per cent of mankind, so that "locally" refers to the other 90 per cent. As we have indicated above, the populations of the Western Hemisphere are increasing so rapidly that the phrase "Western rates" conveys a misconception. Though science opens up such vistas as to deny the pessimistic view of the earth's incapacity to support its inhabitants, we are compelled to remind ourselves that within recent decades the advances made possible by science have been more than counterbalanced by the increases in the world family, and that an advance made in one field seems only too often to be offset by nature getting the upper hand in another. The struggle remains a constant one.

MAN-MADE BARRIERS

Again and again we find ourselves, when talking about possible lines of progress and development, assuming the existence of a world where there is freedom of movement between nation and nation and a ready distribution not only of the discoveries of science and all the means of their application, but also of the resultant products. In actual fact the world position is very different. It is sharply divided by man-made barriers.

In the first place there is the Iron Curtain, enclosing within its formidable barrier the U.S.S.R. and its Communist-dominated satellites. Throughout the preceding chapters we have been compelled for the most part to ignore the countries within the Iron Curtain, the Russians having seen fit not to release statistics of population, cultivation, or other details to permit comparison with other parts of the world. The U.S.S.R.[6] itself is an area of enormous size—eight and three-quarter million square miles; with its satellite countries, excluding China, it controls some 11 million square miles of the earth's surface, about one-fifth of the whole. No part of this vast area approaches the equatorial regions, and no part is truly tropical (unless one now includes China), though with the help of irrigation the lands of Russian Turkistan, hot and dry in summer, can be, and have been, used to produce a variety of tropical crops. The mineral resources of Russia are vast and are still being explored, and we may hazard a guess that the lands within the Iron Curtain form a unit as nearly self-contained economically as they are politically. In any case we are compelled to look at the rest of the world excluding the Russian lands.

In the second place there is the territory of the United States with Alaska, the 3,600,000 square miles within the Dollar Curtain. From certain points of view it must be admitted that the Dollar Curtain is as effective a barrier as the Iron Curtain. In broad, general terms, Canada too lies within the Dollar Curtain, but with closer relationships, economically as well as politically, with the outside world. I shall not attempt in my own words to explain the dilemma of the United States; I shall leave that to an American, C. Lester Walker. He has ably summarized the position for the general reader in an article in the *American Mercury* (Dec., 1949) under the title: "No Wonder the World Is Short of Dollars." In large measure the result of a position forced on her by two world wars, in part the result of the restless urge to find a substitute for anything which cannot be home-produced, the United States has reached the fantastic level of self-sufficiency wherein she produces ninety-four per cent or more of all goods consumed within the country, and with one-sixteenth of the world's population is producing nearly one-third of the world's goods. Synthetic rubber has replaced the import of natural rubber from Southeast Asia, synthetic mica the natural product from India [the production of synthetic mica is, in fact, still in the laboratory stage], synthetic nitrate the natural product from Chile, nylon the silk from Japan and China, tough paper the jute from India, synthetic cryolite the natural mineral from Greenland. The home-produced article has now replaced more or less completely the once large imports of dye stuffs, optical glass and toys (from Germany), watches (Switzerland), chewing gum (Mexico), cigarette paper (France), bristles (China), insecticides (East Africa), and many others. Home agricultural developments have affected almost every part of the world— as with soybeans (formerly entirely from Manchuria), figs (Turkey), currants, sultanas and raisins (Greece, Turkey), wines (Spain and France), sugar (West Indies), dates (Iraq and North Africa), and rice (Southeast Asia).

All the countries mentioned, because they no longer sell their products to America for dollars, no longer have dollars to spend on American products. To make matters worse, the majority of American industrial enterprises have been developed with a production capacity greater than that needed to supply the home market and hence with a need to export. Home industrial production has been built up behind a protective tariff and, far from the barrier being eliminated, it has recently been extended, for example to shipping, by guaranteeing that a minimum proportion of foreign trade be carried in American ships.

Side by side with this development is an embarrassing overproduction of agricultural commodities—a story of plenty which once again seems doomed to deterioration, decay, and destruction in the midst of a hungry, sometimes starving, world. This is the way in which the position was presented to millions of readers through the magazine *Fortune* in January, 1950, relayed by the *Reader's Digest* in April, 1950.

"The U. S. Government's farm price-support program . . . has erected a falsework of bogus values under the whole farm economy, which would collapse into ruin if the support were suddenly removed. It is forcing farmers to produce wildly in excess of any reasonable American capacity to consume. . . . The Government lost 204 million dollars by destroying potatoes or selling them for less than the price of their bags . . . fed millions of dollars' worth of California raisins to hogs. The United States Commodity Credit Corporation is left with a fantastic two-billion dollar inventory:

nearly 5,000,000 bales of cotton . . . worth about $750,000,000

nearly 400,000,000 bushels of wheat costing around $900,000,000

nearly 600,000,000 bushels of corn worth around $900,000,000

more than 70,000,000 lbs. of dried eggs costing close to $100,000,000

more than 100,000,000 lbs. of butter costing more than $60,000,000

about 250,000,000 lbs. of dried milk worth over $30,000,000

huge stocks of tobacco, . . . dried fruit, turpentine and rosin, . . . wool, soybeans, turkeys, [and] peanuts . . ."

"There is little hope that CCC's colossal inventory will melt away. On the contrary, present farm policies are bound to increase it. . . . The Department of Agriculture's other solution is to limit output. . . . The Department has asked farmers to cut acreage of wheat, cotton, potatoes, peanuts, and tobacco, but whether this will cut production is another thing. Better seed and more fertilizer may well maintain output despite somewhat smaller acreage." [7]

All this is happening within the Dollar Curtain, and it seems to bear no relationship to the position in the rest of the world. Over the same period there is no doubt whatever that uncounted thousands died of malnutrition or starvation in Africa and Asia. Even the British housewife was unable to buy, at any price, through ordinary trade channels, a single pound of those California raisins.

It is not my purpose in this book, even if I were able,

to give the answers to these questions. I am concerned rather with the statement of facts. It does seem obvious, however, that this volume of American food can only be used by the hungry world in proportion as America buys from overseas with the utmost freedom and removes tariff barriers to imports.

Outside the Iron Curtain and the Dollar Curtain we still find an abundance of man-made barriers—tariff walls of varying heights, or fences between one country and another. It is quite refreshing to find even three small units, such as the Netherlands, Belgium, and Luxembourg, uniting in a customs union as the Benelux countries. Yet examined in detail there is nearly always a valid reason for the institution of this import duty or that, for the maintenance of this currency restriction or that, and we notice in particular the dilemma of Britain. As a Britisher I always find it difficult to realize that in America I am regarded as a European. Continental Europe is more remote from me in thought, in language, in culture, in economic organization than either Canada or the United States. This, of course, is the fundamental difficulty in the achievement of a Western European Union, which from the American side of the Atlantic looks so obvious. Because of the closeness of the bond within the British Commonwealth of Nations, resulting not only from a broad common origin for so many of the people, strengthened by a common outlook in democratic ideals and fixed in the person of one head, His Majesty the King, the more natural union of Britain remains, as I see it, with the far-flung lands of the Commonwealth. The obvious problem is to prevent a clash between this as an ideal, Western European Union as an ideal, North Atlantic Union as an ideal, and World Free Trade as an ideal.

As regards the first of these ideals, I am, of course, familiar with the widely held view that the British Empire, or the British Commonwealth, is breaking up. As I have said on many previous occasions, when a family grows up and the members in turn assume the management of their own separate homes one does not talk about the "break-up of the family"; rather does one point to the success of the parents as measured by the success of their children, and their children's children. I see the evolution of the British Commonwealth in this light.

In the meantime, Britain is deeply concerned with helping the underdeveloped lands, notably Africa, toward their eventual independence, and through its Colonial Office is vitally concerned with colonial development. It was in 1929 that the British government established by Act of Parliament a Colonial Development Fund and the quotation on the second page of this book is from the revision of that Act made in the summer of 1940, an optimistic statement in the darkest days of the war. Later, increased grants were made so that for the ten-year period ending March, 1956, the allocation for development, welfare, and research was £120,000,000 ($336,000,000). The plans formulated by the British government for the underdeveloped colonial areas resemble those of the Marshall Plan for Europe;

they are designed essentially to help the areas concerned to stand on their own feet. It seems therefore vitally important that the good start which has been made in Anglo-American cooperation in the development of these tropical lands should be continued. It should have been made abundantly clear in what has been said that the task will call for all our united knowledge and concentration of purpose.

It was an important part of the Marshall Plan from its inception that the program of the Economic Cooperation Administration should cover the "dependent overseas territories" (a term which avoided the word "colonies") of Belgium, France, the Netherlands, Portugal, and the United Kingdom. Professor J. E. Orchard has summarized in the *Geographical Review* for January, 1951, the many projects in which ECA is interested—in 85 separate countries or units covering 8,900,-000 square miles and 170,000,000 people in Africa, Southeast Asia, and the Caribbean. The long-term development projects are estimated to cost $7,500,000,000, with communications and agriculture taking the lion's share and with more than a third of the total expenditure in tropical Africa. The work antedates, and is independent of, the Point IV program but works in close liaison to avoid overlapping. Primarily the aim is to help the underdeveloped countries to help themselves and in so doing America is dealing a powerful blow against Communistic influences—a more important objective than the incidental increase in world supplies of certain raw materials.

CHAPTER VIII

Some Conclusions and Speculations

IN THE preceding chapters every effort has been made to give essential facts and to present an objective interpretation. Reasons are given for believing the mid-century population of the world to be of the order of 2,350,000,000. Reservations are made on account of inadequacy of data, but in all those areas where accurate census statistics are available, there is no possible doubt as to the rapidity of present population growth. The years since the end of World War II have produced many surprises such as a crude birth rate in the United States practically equaling that of India in 1947 and the rate of net increase considerably greater over the period 1937 to 1947. The marked postwar increase in birth rates, a sort of catching up on deferred family planning, has led demographers to look for a new basis, that of total family, on which to make their forecasts rather than to place reliance on annual figures. There is no doubt that, whatever the causes, the confident estimates made in the nineteen-thirties of coming population declines have proved wide of the mark.[1] While the popular concept of the "teeming millions" of India and China, some forty per cent of all mankind, may be true enough, other widely held beliefs are far from true. The high rates of population increase are not there or in crowded Europe but in the Americas. What may happen in Africa we do not know: with increasing knowledge and skill in medicine and in agriculture, Africa may well be on the verge of great increases in population, but in the past that continent has lost ground relatively. It is the English-speaking whites who have increased four times as rapidly as the peoples of the world as a whole.

The average density of the world's population is of the order of 42 persons a square mile or roughly the actual density in the continental United States. Thus 14 or 15 acres are the share of each individual in the land surface of the globe. If we eliminate the areas where physical conditions are such that close settlement must remain unachieved, the share of the individual in what remains is reduced to 4 or 5 acres. This includes the great problem lands of the tropics. The hot, wet, rain forests of the Amazon and the Congo and the alternately sun-baked and rain-drenched savanna lands are included in this total. Despite our boasts, we do not yet know how to handle these lands so as to make them, if they can be made, permanently productive for mankind. The optimists include them, and there is often a surprising similarity between present assessments of their values and older assessments of other lands which still remain unproductive after a hundred years or more. The pessimists, on the other hand, find that there

is only a little more than one acre of productive plowable land in the world per head of population and
much of that is deteriorating through misuse.

It is certainly true that in country after country of
the Old World, if we eliminate mountain areas and
land excluded from agricultural statistics, there is less
than two acres of land of all types per person to serve
the needs of the population. In other words, population
density exceeds 320 a square mile over land which can
be considered, even on the most liberal interpretation,
as actually or potentially productive.

This fact, rather than any deep-seated belief in one
political ideology more than another, is behind the
drive towards land planning and a balanced use of
natural resources. Where the land shortage is desperate
and hunger as well as poverty is a reality or but a step
away, peoples will naturally cling to any straw—whether
it is labeled fascism or communism—in the hope of salvation.

The inexorable machinations of fate have thrown the
United States into a position of world leadership; as I
have ventured to suggest, the head of a dollar empire
more powerful than any empire the world has yet
known. It is quite impossible to escape the responsibilities which result. In its own sphere the British Commonwealth has long had and known, even if it may
not have adequately handled, these world problems
and responsibilities. In both cases leadership has been
hampered by insufficient knowledge.

WHERE ARE THE UNDERDEVELOPED LANDS?

Is it possible to indicate now where the underdeveloped lands are actually situated?

The first truth which seems to my mind to emerge is that from all points of view it is an easier task to increase production from the mid-latitude or temperate lands where we are familiar with the vagaries of nature and where we know something of the management of soils and the development of crops than it is to look for immediate development of tropical lands. In this sense the great underdeveloped lands of the world as indicated by low outputs per acre must be held to include large parts of the United States,[2] Canada, Argentina, and Australia. Here the line of progress seems to be an increase in output per unit-area to levels comparable with those in the most highly productive parts of northwestern Europe. Any such development must be accompanied by a willingness to foster both international population movements and international trade, that is, the abolition of restrictions.

In the second place, can we determine where the underdeveloped lands in the tropics are? An interesting approach is that known as the sieve method. We take out of the tropical lands all parts which have a mountainous, broken, or otherwise unsuitable terrain; then those parts too dry to be capable of cultivation and development; then other parts where soil is deficient in quantity or quality, and so on. At least this method has the advantage that it forces attention on potential areas.

What is the present position and what are the adverse factors? This is where we realize how serious is our present ignorance. Actually we cannot use the sieve method because the information is not available. Always cutting across estimates based on actual or potential production of food, we have the very different pattern of world resources of power and minerals. The rich, still hidden it may be, resources of the underdeveloped lands put many of them in a potentially strong world position.

POINT IV

The assertion of Point IV quoted in the beginning of this book that "humanity possesses the knowledge and the skill to relieve the suffering of these people," that is of underdeveloped areas where food is inadequate, cannot be taken literally. As I stress above, our knowledge, especially of land-use, is woefully inadequate. The destruction wrought over the past century by our modern machinery on the earth's natural resources is so colossal, so staggering, that if unchecked it can lead to the suicide of the whole human race. With our own problems of soil conservation but partly solved and the practice of types of balanced mixed farming which conserve rather than destroy the land by no means generally accepted, we contemplate turning loose the same old forces of destruction on the still unknown tropical lands. When we have learned to protect our own poor, naked, suffering soils with a mantle of grass and trees, when we desist from thrashing the life out of our middle-latitude lands by continuous plowing and mono-culture, when, in other words, we have taken steps to cast out the beam which is within our own eye, we shall be in a better position to deal with the mote in our brother's eye.

The survey of world conditions in Chapter III points to the countries of northwestern Europe—Denmark, the Netherlands, England—as those enjoying a high stand-ard of living, an unparalleled high level of agricultural output per unit-area, a steadily improving soil, and a complete absence of soil erosion. This suggests that balanced mixed farming, with rotation of crops and carefully managed permanent pasture, with relatively small ten-acre fields but a high degree of mechanization, is the best answer for the world as a whole, that it is the solution to the problem of preserving the new lands of middle latitudes, and, in due course and suitably modified through research and experimentation, of lands yet to be tamed in the tropics.

In the meantime let us approach the problems in the tropics with due humility: there is much to be learned before we can teach.

The geographer's special field of survey and analysis has here a vital contribution to make—through a world land-use survey. The problem of the underdeveloped lands is not one to be solved by some act of govern-ment of this or any other country. It is a problem which will remain with us for decades, for generations to come, presenting us with a continuous challenge.

WHAT POPULATION CAN THE WORLD SUPPORT?

Sooner or later the question is always posed: What population can or could the world support? To this there is no answer: the unknown factors are too numerous. When, however, we come to the ability of individual countries to produce food and so to support a population, there is a line of approach which I find interesting. If we take northwestern Europe as a starting point, where, as we have noted, the general standard of living is high and the efficiency of farming is such that the output per acre is as high as anywhere in the world, we find that, very roughly, one acre of improved farm land will support one human being. The countries mentioned are favored by nature in some ways, but not in all. For example, Denmark has mostly poor soils, England lacks sunshine and has very varied soils, and so on. We are surely entitled to see what would happen if other parts of the world were farmed as efficiently at our *present* standard of knowledge on *existing* acreages of farmland only. There is no recourse to hydroponics or hypothetical types of farming nor to expenditures on fertilizers which would be unjustified by the law of diminishing returns, but simply a thorough-going application of known principles of good husbandry. On this basis, with 24 million acres, plus another half million obtained by converting 5 million acres of rough grazing as equivalent to 500,000 of improved land, we realize that England and Wales could support a population of 24½ million people. The actual population is 44 million, so that England and Wales as an example comes nowhere near self-sufficiency. If we take the actual cultivated area of Canada at 90 million acres and presume this to be capable of the same level of production as northwestern Europe, we can postulate a potential population which could be fully supported from the land of Canada itself at 90 million, against the present 14 million. On the one hand this does not take into account the still unoccupied lands which can be settled and developed and which are vast in extent, but on the other hand it does not take into account the fact that the Dominion of Canada exports foodstuffs and raw materials to the overpopulated parts of the world, including Britain. On this same basis the existing farmlands of the United States, taking only cropland and plowable pasture and ignoring all the rest, could easily support a population of 500 million, against the present total of 150 million; and Russia 556 million, against the present 200 million. It may perhaps be dangerous to go on with this generalization, but it is difficult to claim that any of the new lands in mid-latitudes are fully developed in the sense that they carry the population they are able by their natural endowments to support.

Table XX shows possibilities of potential population in selected countries. On the basis here used the area of the world at present cultivated could support, if fully farmed by known best methods, at least 3 billion people on an adequate nutritional standard. If the lands at present unused or inadequately used could be brought

TABLE XX. ACTUAL AND POTENTIAL POPULATION SUPPORTABLE FROM LAND RESOURCES

Area in thousands of acres; population in thousands

	Total area	Improved farmland	Population Actual	Population ·Potential
Denmark	10,500	7,500	4,200	7,500
Netherlands	10,000	6,000	10,000	6,000
England and Wales	37,000	24,500	44,500	24,500
France	137,500	51,000 b	41,500	51,000
Italy	123,500	38,000 b	46,000	38,000
Canada	2,460,000	90,000 e	13,000	90,000
United States	1,900,000	500,000 e	150,000	500,000
Argentina	712,000	75,000 e	16,000	75,000
India and Pakistan a	1,012,000	330,000 d	420,000 a	330,000
Burma	167,000	21,000 e	17,000 a	21,000+
Japan	168,000	12,500 e	90,000	12,500+
New Zealand	66,000	19,125	2,000	19,125
Australia	1,900,000	29,000	8,000	29,000
U.S.S.R.	5,590,000	556,000 e	200,000 a	556,000

a Rough estimates.
b Existing arable and tree crops only.
e Arable only.
d Crops and fallow.
e Cropland and plowable pasture.
If pasture (improved) is added to arable the figure for Italy becomes 51,000,000 and for France 81,000,000 acres.

into production on the same basis, potential world population climbs to over the 10 billion mark.

At the same time science is adding constantly to the sum of human knowledge, and there is every reason to expect advances which will simplify the problems of feeding the human race—if only man can overcome the barriers he himself has erected between the nations.

Notes

CHAPTER II

[1] Population and Human Destiny, *World Review*, Jan., 1950, pp. 7-14.
[2] "By race is meant no more than the fact that it is possible to make a very rough classification of mankind into white, black, brown, yellow and red." Carr-Saunders, *op. cit.*, p. 44.
[3] 1940-41 figures are used throughout this section because 1950-51 figures are not yet available. Some later calculations are given below.
[4] *Sterben die Weissen Völker?*, 1934.
[5] "The Numbers and Distribution of Mankind," *Scientific Monthly*, LXIV (1947), 389-96.

CHAPTER III

[1] "The Extent of the Cultivable Land," *Geographical Journal*, LXXVI (1930), 504-09.
[2] "Adjustment of Agriculture to Its Environment (Presidential Address)," *Annals of the Association of American Geographers*, XXXIII (1943), 163-93. His authoritative source was the U. S. Department of Agriculture, Bureau of Agricultural Economics, "Estimates of Quantities of Food Necessary to Provide Certain Specified Diets and Crop Acreages and Numbers of Livestock Required for Indicated Production," prepared by O. V. Wells.
[3] See, for instance: C. W. Thornthwaite, "Problems in the Classification of Climates," *Geographical Review*, XXXIII (1943), 233-55; *idem:* "An Approach towards a Rational Classification of Climate," *ibid.,* XXXVIII (1948), 55-94. Thornthwaite's own classification in its latest version, the key to which is the measurement of precipitation efficiency, involves a considerable amount of mathematical calculation, not easy for the layman to understand. When his system is worked out for the continents, as is now being done at the School of Geography of Clark University under the direction of Dr. S. Van Valkenburg, we can begin a really satisfactory approach to the problem of which of the uncultivated lands of the world are cultivable.

4 Sir Samuel Baker, *Eight Years in Ceylon* (London, 1855), pp. 53-58.

5 "Report of a Survey of Problems in the Mechanization of Native Agriculture in Tropical African Colonies," *Colonial Advisory Council of Agriculture, Animal Health and Forestry, No. 1, 1950.*

6 See *inter alia* the "Reports of Conferences" at Yangambi (Semaine Agricole de Yangambi, *Institut National pour l'Étude Agronomique du Congo Belge*, Pts. I and II, 1947), at Goma (*Bulletin Agricole du Congo Belge*, Pts. I, II, III, 1949), and Jos (British African Land Utilization Conference, Jos, Nigeria, Nov., 1949; *Final Report* printed in Zaria, Nigeria, for the Conference.)

7 Th. Monod, "Two African International Scientific Conferences," *Geographical Review*, XL (1950), 309-12.

8 *The Times Weekly Edition*, London: March 14, 1951.

9 Frank Debenham, "Report on the Water Resources of the Bechuanaland Protectorate, Northern Rhodesia, The Nyasaland Protectorate, Tanganyika Territory, Kenya, and the Uganda Protectorate," *Colonial Research Publications*, No. 2, 1948.

10 In "Aiding Underdeveloped Areas Abroad," *Annals of The American Academy of Political and Social Science*, CCLXVIII (1950), 85-95; ref. on p. 88. See also Douglas D. Crary, "Recent Agricultural Developments in Saudi Arabia," *Geographical Review*, XLI (1951), 366-383.

11 Dr. P. Lamartine Yates calculated the "farm population" in Belgium at 85 a square mile, in Denmark at 40. *Food Production in Western Europe* (1940).

Chapter IV

1 *Chronica Botanica*, XI (1948), 4.

2 *Future Food and Agriculture Policy*, 1948.

3 See the table quoted by F. Le Gros Clark: *Feeding the Human Family*, (London, 1947), p. 31.

4 "Population and Food Supply: The Current Scare," *Scientific Monthly*, LXVIII (1949), 17-26, with bibliography.

5 The work of the International Institute of Agriculture at Rome has been taken over by the Food and Agriculture Organization of the United Nations and the invaluable *International Yearbook of Agricultural Statistics* now appears as the *Yearbook of Food and Agricultural Statistics* from Washington, D.C. The tables are far from complete, notably in the absence of any returns from the U.S.S.R., but for each of the other principal countries area harvested, production, and yield are given in metric measures.

6 *Journal of the Royal Statistical Society*, CII (1939), 21-62.

7 The caloric output per acre may be simply calculated for the cereals. A bushel of wheat of sixty pounds (at 3,640 calories per kilogram or 1,650 calories per pound) is equivalent to 99,000 or, say, 100,000 calories. The 1934-38 world average of fifteen bushels per acre represents 1.5

million calories an acre a year; the British output of thirty-five bushels, 3.5 million calories. A daily intake of 2,500 calories or 912,500 a year confirms figures given above that at world yields half an acre does not afford an adequate diet, whereas a well-farmed acre of wheat land in Britain provides adequately for 3.5 persons.

[8] As mentioned previously, the positions of the United States and Canada in 1934-38 are affected by the abnormally bad year 1934, but 1946 was also a bad harvest year in some countries.

[9] J. R. Currie and W. H. Long, *An Agricultural Survey in South Devon*, 1929. Out of an average of 205 farms the total net cash income of the farmer and his family was £2 a week, $10.00 at the rate of exchange then current.

Chapter V

[1] In the *World Geography of Petroleum*, published by the American Geographical Society in 1950 is a map (Pl. I, facing p. 14) showing the sedimentary basins, which may be regarded as the world's potential oil-field areas, though very many basins are without oil. The map suggests possibilities in French North Africa—they are being explored with the assistance of ECA—but little elsewhere in the African continent.

[2] "The Petroleum and Natural Gas Conservation Board estimated Alberta oil resources at the end of 1950 at 923 million barrels. . . . Unofficial estimates go as high as ten and twenty billion barrels, and certainly not less than five billion. They base their figures on the probability of new discoveries resulting from the current record-breaking exploration programmes." Gordon McCaffrey, "Major Oilfield Discoveries in Western Canada," *New Commonwealth*, (March, 1951), pp. 412-17.

[3] "Colonial Development," *Journal of the Royal Society of Arts*, XCVII (1949), 834-49.

Chapter VI

[1] *Journal of the Town Planning Institute* (London, 1950), XXXVI, 141-52.

[2] "The Economics of Freedom from Want," *Chronica Botanica*, II (1948), 259-70.

Chapter VII

[1] See J. W. Watson: "Forest or Bog: Man the Deciding Factor," *Scottish Geographical Magazine*, Vol. 55, 1939, pp. 148-161.

[2] For illustrations see L. Dudley Stamp, "Land Utilization and Soil Erosion in Nigeria," *Geographical Review*, XXVIII (1938), 32-45.

[3] The commission was under the chairmanship of Dr. S. Van Valken-

burg of Clark University; the other members were Professor Hans Boesch of Zurich, Dr. Leo Waibel, who came fresh from his recent years of work in Brazil, and the writer. The commission was assisted in its deliberations by a dozen experts, who kindly acted as witnesses.

4 For many other examples see Jacques M. May, "Medical Geography: Its Methods and Objectives," *Geographical Review,* XL (1950), 9-41.

5 Minerals in the soil, appearing in very small quantities, which are nevertheless essential for healthful plant growth.

6 FAO, *Yearbook of Agricultural Statistics for 1949* gives the following for the U.S.S.R. in acres for 1947: arable land, 555,750,000; meadow land, 306,280,000; forest, 1,551,160,000; unused, potentially usable, 29,640,000; other land, 3,146,780,000.

7 By special permission of the editors of *Fortune.*

CHAPTER VIII

1 Nevertheless they are still being made. "Obviously," said Kingsley Davis to the Inter-American Conference on Conservation of Renewable Natural Resources at Denver in September, 1948, "both the United States and Canada are reaching the end of their period of rapid population growth . . . in the 1990-2000 decade there will be no growth at all but a loss in population."

2 Black and Kiefer in *Future Food and Agriculture Policy* (*op. cit.,* p. 91) approach the problem from a different angle but reach the conclusion "If the land of the United States were in Europe, probably some 700 million acres would be cropped in some sort of rotation" (p. 138).

Index

Food: equatorial crops, 63; purposes of, 85-88; caloric intake, 87; nutritional problems, 88; production estimates, 89; production by countries, 92-98; increased yields, 96, 97; fish, 110

France, 29, 48, 101, 104, 126, 137, 147, 205, 210; population of, 36

Fuel resources, 124, 126-129

Gambia experiment, 73-77

Geneiri, 73, 74

Geographical Review, 13

Geographical Situation of the United States in Relation to World Policies, 138

Geological structure, 130

Germany, 33, 101, 104, 119, 126, 137, 139, 205; population, 36

Global area, 48

Gold: Yukon, 131; California, 136; Africa, 137, 145

Gold Coast, 139, 144, 145

Great Britain, 24, 37, 39, 101, 107, 110, 113, 126, 132, 137, 146, 149, 172, 210; population, 36; wartime farm organization, 163, 164; present farm problems, 164-169; national land-planning; *see* Land-planning

Greece, 99, 205

Greenland, 205

Groundnut Scheme, 65, 71-72

Habitable area, 48, 51, 52, 53, 54

Hanson, Earl, 62

Herbertson, A. J., 55, 57

Highland areas, 49

Holland; *see* Netherlands

Hoskins, H. L., 79

Huntington and Van Valkenburg, 99

Huxley, Julian, 23, 24, 27

Hylea Research Institute, 66

Iceland, 33

Income per capita, 12

India, 8, 12, 17, 25, 26, 33, 39, 43, 77, 83, 97, 101, 104, 107, 126, 144, 172, 173, 205; population, 36; land use in, 169; agricultural problems, 171

Indiana University, 8

Indochina, 172

Indonesia, 143, 172

INÉAC, 66

Inhabited areas, 52, 53

International Geographical Congress, 187

International Geological Congress, 119

International Institute of Statistics, 20

Iran, 79, 129

Iraq, 79, 129, 205

Iron, 138, 145

Iron Curtain, 203

Israel, 36

Italy, 101, 104, 147, 148, 185; population, 36

Jacks, G. V., 179

Japan, 43, 101, 104, 126, 205; population, 36

Java, 33, 64, 83; agricultural efficiency, 114

Kariba Gorge scheme, 77

Kendall, M. G., 99

Kenya, 71

Kiefer, M. E., 91

Korea, 144; population, 36

Krug, J. A., 11